DEVON'S LAST 'METAL' MINE
GREAT ROCK 'SHINY' ORE MINE

With brief histories of other 'shiny' ore mines
of the Hennock/Bovey Tracey area

by
Tony Brooks

With contributions by Kris Apps
and Dr Richard Scrivener

CORNISH HILLSIDE PUBLICATIONS
St Austell, Cornwall

In memory of Anthony Haydon-Baillie, 1942-1964

First published 2004 by
Cornish Hillside Publications
St Austell, Cornwall

ISBN: 1 900147 335 (Clothbound)
ISBN: 1 900147 327 (Paperback)

Design/setting by
The Design Field
www.thedesignfield.com

Printed by Short Run Press, Exeter, Devon

INTRODUCTION

This is the story of Devon's last 'metal' mine. It's history certainly goes well back into the 19th Century, but its main period of production was from about 1900 up until it finally closed in 1969.

Most mines in the South West of England are well documented, the local Record Offices holding mine plans, cost books etc. and the Mining Journal is full of references, annual reports and articles. Not so Great Rock. There are no company records. There is very little in print and it seems to have been largely neglected by the many photographers who have recorded images of the industry. Perhaps it was too small, employing at its peak only some 20 men. Perhaps it was too isolated, tucked away in the woods outside the rarely visited village of Hennock in Devon. After the Second World War, when most mines were looking to replace steam power with electricity, Great Rock was still largely water powered. It never used steam power and had no mains electricity until about 1950. Where else in the UK, in the second half of the 20th Century, would you have found a mine where they made their own locomotives and wagons, where water was supplied through a half-mile wooden launder and where, one night, a changeroom-cum-mess hut blew up?

I have to declare an interest. I worked underground at Great Rock for two weeks in the Spring of 1963. I was then a very green mining student, but I will remember the experience for ever. It is impossible properly to describe what it was like – you had to work there to appreciate it. In 40 years of mining I have never come across a mine like Great Rock. I got the job at Great Rock through Tony Haydon-Baillie, who with his younger brother Wensley, had worked on the mine in 1962. It was Tony who took a number of photographs at the mine in 1962/63 which appear in this book. He and I had both started on the mining course at the Camborne School of Mines in September 1962. Unfortunately Tony's examination results were disappointing and he left at the end of that first term. In March 1963 he went to work in Canada where, tragically, he was killed in a car accident 12 months later.

Whilst I have used information from a large number of sources, I anticipate that more information will come to light in the future. I have tried, where possible, to reference these sources as future researchers may need to reassess these in the light of new information. I have made use of many taped interviews made with former employees. These interviews of men and women, many now sadly passed away, give us a glimpse of the mine as seen through their eyes. Human memory is fallible and, in serious research, is no substitute for accurate written reports and records. However, in the absence of any proper records they are invaluable and they add colour to the story. Listening to the tapes one gets a sense of genuine lovely people – most with a real enthusiasm for the mine. In many cases, rather than paraphrase, I have quoted verbatim from these interviews. This removes some of the interpretation bias that I might subconsciously add, and anyway who is better able to describe what happened than the people who actually experienced it? I feel privileged to have been able to record some of their memories in this book.

When you see an illustration of the most photographed bridge in the world over Sydney Harbour, give a thought to the fact that somewhere in the layers of paint that protect it is a bit of Devon. Brunel's Albert Bridge, that links Cornwall & Devon also used paint containing 'micaceous haematite' from mines like Great Rock.

Brunel's Albert Bridge (© Royal Institution of Cornwall)

Acknowledgements

This book could not have been written without the help, encouragement and enthusiasm of many people including:

Chrissie Le Marchant who recorded interviews with a number of ex-Great Rock employees in 1984 as part of a project for the Dartmoor National Park. I have drawn heavily on these interviews for this book. I also acknowledge the efforts of Tess Walker, of the Dartmoor National Park, for arranging for me to have permission to use these audio tapes.

The Kelly Mine Preservation Society's (KMPS) monthly newsletters. Over the years, as information has come to light through research, it has been recorded in the pages of the newsletter. I am grateful for permission to use their material. Regular contributors – Doug Westaway, Brian Brett and Nick Walter deserve a special mention. They have also given me much additional advice and information.

Justin Brooke – as always generously gave me full access to his extensive files.

Bob Le Marchant – mining engineer and enthusiast with whom I 're-discovered' the mine in 1983.

Mick Atkinson and Chris Schmitz for notes and correspondence.

The late Frank Bice Michell ACSM, former lecturer, Vice-Principal of the Camborne School of Mines and consultant to Great Rock.

The late Norman Bennett, formerly a Director of the Ferrubron Manufacturing Co., for much information in correspondence from his home in Malta.

D M Bishop for copies of his correspondence with Norman Bennett and permission to quote from his articles in the Journal of the Oil and Colour Chemists Association.

Keith Loze for permission to use his article on the use of carbide lamps at Great Rock, for photographs and general encouragement.

P.H.G.Richardson of Totnes, for photographs and permission to quote from his book 'Mines of Dartmoor and the Tamar Valley'.

Dr Richard Scrivener for writing the chapter on the geology and for allowing me to have access to the Great Rock files held at the British Geological Survey in Exeter.

The late Mr Sydney Taylor, then the Mine Manager, for giving me a job in 1963.

The late Mrs Murray-Lee of Yonder Wreyland, Lustleigh (Tony Haydon-Baillie's mother and great supporter of his interest in mining) for putting me up during my time at Great Rock in 1963.

John Manley, Sid Preston's grandson for photographs and memories from his mother.

Ron F.Tucker, the fourth generation of the Tucker family to have a connection with the mine, for his memories, for checking some of the text, and for permission to use photographs from his grandfather's collection.

Arthur Ball, formerly the Mine's engineer, for checking some of the text and who drew, from memory, many of the diagrams of plant and equipment which I have included in this book.

And finally, Kris & Bernard Apps, who at the time of writing (2003) are resident in the mine bungalow. They have always shown enthusiasm for the mine and the village. Kris wrote the chapter on Hennock village and has contributed to the chapter on the People of Great Rock Mine.

Photographs not already acknowledged above – British Geological Survey; Roger Burt; Devon County Records Office; Ralph Finch; John Hamilton; Kelly Mine Preservation Society; Mike Messenger; South Devon Journal; Station Pictures – Vic Mitchell (reproduced from 'Branch Line to Mortonhampstead' Middleton Press); John Watton. Photographs are also individually acknowledged in the List of Plates.

CONTENTS

LIST OF FIGURES

LIST OF PLATES

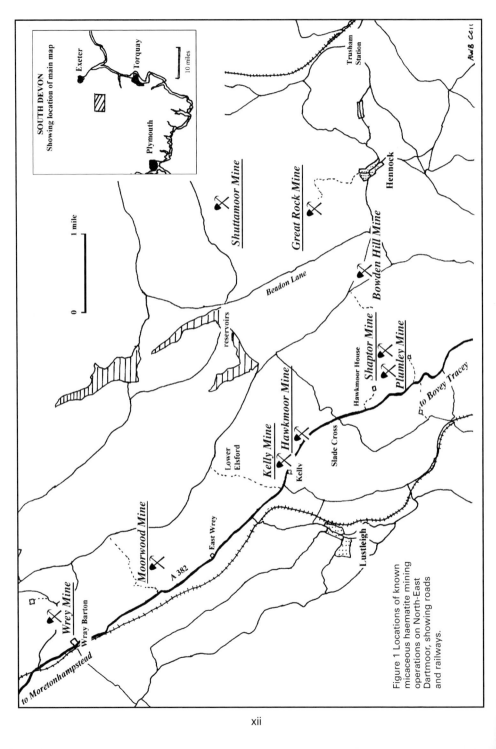

Figure 1 Locations of known micaceous haematite mining operations on North-East Dartmoor, showing roads and railways.

CHAPTER ONE

EARLY HISTORY OF MICACEOUS HAEMATITE PRODUCTION IN DEVON

Iron oxide in the form of a shiny mineral known as micaceous haematite has been extracted from the Hennock area of Devon for over 200 years – See **Figure 1**. opposite.

Information on the period up to about 1890 is sketchy and incomplete. From what is available, I have been unable to establish with any certainty when mining at Great Rock first started. The following is a record of what is known of mining in the area.

The first written reference is reported by Cecil Torr[1] in the Wreyland documents[2] when

> *On 24 June 1797 the tenement called South Kelly and the tenement called Leigh were sold by John Pinsent for £2152 10s. to George Wills of Rudge in the Parish of Lustleigh.......On the same day, 24 June 1797, George Wills leased to John Pinsent for twenty-one years 'a certain mine of black lead or some other mineral substance' in South Kelly.*

One gets the impression that this was a 'lease-back' of an existing operation which Pinsent did not wish to relinquish.

South Kelly was on the site now occupied by the present Kelly Farm and thus we can assume that micaceous haematite was then being produced from the lodes of what is now known as the **Kelly Mine**. Indications that production from the area, but not necessarily Kelly, had started some time earlier have been identified by Peter Roberts of the Kelly Mine Preservation Society (KMPS) from evidence in the Court Entries of the Borough of Ashburton 1747-1805.

> *These are contained in a vellum bound volume of 12.75 x 8 inches pages. When examining these volumes in strong light glistening specks will be seen adhering to the pages where the writing is heavy. This is especially true for the years from 1765 to 1784, and is proof that blotting was being achieved at that time by the use of Devon Writing Sand[a] which was obtained from Micaceous Haematite.[3]*

[a] Writing sand or pounce, was a fine powder formerly used to prevent ink from spreading on unsized paper.

A mine for a substance resembling pulverised plumbago[b] which is identifiable as micaceous haematite is mentioned in the travel diary of Svedenstierna in 1802 but the exact location was not given.[4]

There is now a gap of some 20 years before Lysons, writing in 1822, commented on a specular iron lode, two feet wide, in granite, in the parish of Hennock.[5] It is nor clear whether Lysons really meant specular iron which is a hard crystalline variety of haematite or micaceous haematite which is a soft foliaceous variety. Both are iron oxides.

The next mention of this deposit was in 1839 when the geologist De la Beche reported:

> *Micaceous iron-ore is found in various places upon Dartmoor (a vein said to be two feet thick, containing this ore, was found in granite near Hennock); and, under the name of Devonshire sand, was some years since sent to London and used as writing sand, selling from £3 3s. to £8 8s. per ton.*[6]

This latter description is so much like the one by Lysons that we can assume that De la Beche used Lysons as his reference.

The reference to the title 'Hennock' has created all kinds of confusion to later researchers. 19th Century reporters, particularly in the Mining Journal, frequently refer to a mine or mines as being "in the Parish of Hennock"; "near Hennock"; "The Hennock Iron Mine or Mines" etc.. The problem is that a number of micaceous iron ore mines, known today as Kelly, Hawkmoor, Plumley, Shaptor, Bowden Hill and Great Rock, all lay in or near the parish of Hennock.

This confusion is further compounded by the presence of the better documented **Hennock Mine** (NGR 836814) which was a lead mine on the west bank of the Teign near Franklands farm in the east of the parish. This Hennock Mine, later part of the South Exmouth Mine, lay on the southern extremity of two north-south lead lodes that had been worked extensively up the Teign valley towards Bridford. Hamilton Jenkin[7] (1981) reports that it was briefly examined in 1812. The mine was opened up in 1836 on an enlarged sett as the **Wheal Hennock Silver, Lead, Copper and Manganese Mine**.

> *In 1849 a fresh lease was granted to a Mr Vatcher of Exeter who sank a trial shaft a short distance south of the former workings. At the 20 and 30 fm levels the lode displayed values up to £18 worth of lead ore per*

---

[b] Plumbago or Graphite is naturally occurring carbon. It is iron-grey to dark steel-grey in colour. An early source was from Borrowdale in the Lake District from which the local pencil industry developed. Today it is used as a lubricant, in paints and for electrodes in electric furnaces.

fathom and in February 1852 it was decided to purchase a 50-in steam engine. Under the name of South Exmouth (NGR 835 807) working was resumed in 1861 and during the next seven years the mine was developed on a considerable scale......At the height of its activity the mine employed 122 people and in one year showed a profit of £1,500. Notwithstanding this and a recorded output of 760 tons of lead ore and 1,150 ounces of silver between 1862 and 1867 the overall cost of working exceeded returns. As a consequence, operations were abandoned in 1868, when the 50-in. pumping engine, 25-in. steam whim and crusher, together with two water-wheels of 20ft. and 8ft. diameter were offered for sale.

Fortunately, as this was a shaft operation on two north-south lead lodes, it is fairly easy to eliminate most of the references to the mine which occur during this period. However, in July 1857 in an account of iron mines of Dartmoor there is the comment:

Some black ore and shining ore from Hennock, and shining ore from Exmouth Consols...[8]

Whether the Hennock mine mentioned here is the lead mine is open to question, as the reference is clearly historical.

Returning to the micaceous iron ore mines, in April 1841, a advertisement for the sale of ore appeared:

Shining ore for sale – a quantity of this ore, of superior quality, has been raised at Hennock, Devon. Samples may be had, gratis, on application to Mr Wills, Kelly[9]

At that time the Kelly estate, owned by James Wills, included: Tin Hill Coppice (1290), Great Tin Hill (1291), Middle Tin Hill (1294), Tin Field (1298) and Little Tin Hill (1313) which closely corresponds with the position of the present day Kelly mine. The numbers in brackets refer to the field or enclosed areas on the Tithe map of 1841.[10] It is not known whether this ore was obtained from surface pits or from underground mining via adits. However the lodes in this area occur on a steep hillside that would have lent themselves to exploitation by self-draining adits at an early stage.

Shortly before this, in April 1841, a George Perriman leased a property to Joseph Marshall Heath (of the Bristol and Foreign Iron Co.) for 7 years with dues of 2 shillings per 22 hundred weights iron ore and one tenth on other minerals. The lease comprised House Field (1 041 -2), Shaptor Park (1 035),

Shapter Long Field (1046) and Eight Acre Field (912) all part of Higher Bowden Estate, about a mile west of Hennock **Figure 2**. Among the covenants were that not more than two shafts 10 feet square were to be opened in any field and a minimum of four men in each end.

An east-west lode was found in Ten Acre Field at the top of the hill and working started there – this was also known as **Ten Acres Iron Mine**. During the working about 700 tons of rich ore was raised and £70 paid in dues. Operations ceased at Midsummer 1842 when Heath told Perriman that he could not make a profit.

Perriman sued Heath for damages for breakage of covenants.[11] In one field ten pits had been dug, it was claimed, the two largest openworks being 9 feet wide and 160 feet and 130 feet long respectively. Perriman was granted £100 on breach regarding the workings and £5 on the labour. In April 1844 Perriman brought a fresh action for breach of covenant and £125 damages plus £100 per annum for rent was awarded.

It was agreed to allow Heath to mine 1,500 tons of ore per year free of royalty – and work was resumed. In May 1844 a fatal accident occurred:

As W Radmore was working underground in the Ten Acre Iron Mine, the hole in the roof, which he had fired (sic), unexpectedly exploded, occasioning his instant death.[12]

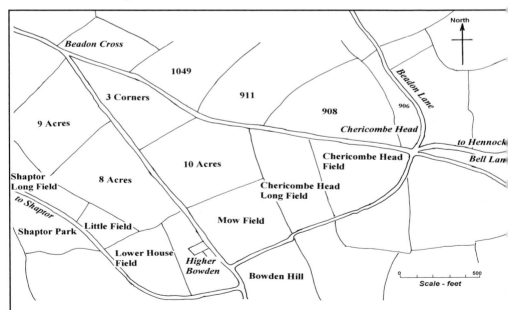

Figure 2 – 1841 Tithe Map of the Higher Bowden Estate

He would have been using gunpowder. One of two things may have happened. Either he lit a home-made fuse which burnt too rapidly setting off the explosive prematurely or, more likely, he had had a hole misfire and had gone back to inspect it only for the charge to explode perhaps caused by a faulty fuse that had burnt too slowly.

In March 1845, a stationary engine was erected to pump the pits but it failed to do so. Work continued until June or July 1845 when the mine was abandoned leaving ten pits in Ten Acres the four longest being 117 feet, 70 feet, 50 feet, and 24 feet long, and the deepest was 25 feet deep. A horse fell into one of the pits here and was killed in 1846.

During the law suits it was revealed that the mine instead of being opened by an adit had been worked opencast with resulting water trouble. One pit had 6 feet of water in it and

...that is where the engine to be turned by wind is.

Presumably they put in some kind of wind pump. The specific nature of the initial lease indicates that the position of the iron lode was already known or at least suspected. **Ten Acre Mine** can be identified as being part of the same sett later known as **Bowden Hill Mine**. The mine lies to the south of the road west out of Hennock. The land here is relatively flat and would have been worked either by lode back pits or open-works or by shallow shafts. Radmore's unfortunate accident tells us that, by 1844, some of the workings were truly underground as he was blasting a hole in the roof of some excavation.

Clearly this working again failed for, in August 1845, George Perriman leased, to Smith Tibbits an ironmaster, part of Higher Bowden estate: Challacombe (Chericombe) Head Field, Challacombe Head Long field, The Mow Field, Three Corners and Ten Acres:

Ten Acres and Challacombe Head Longfield subject to a grant of a right to search for minerals granted to J Marshall Heath and which grant will terminate at Christmas 1847.

The lease was for 21 years at £100 per annum.[13]

Tibbits was also leasing other mine rights for on the 31st December 1847, under the title **Iron Mines Hennock**, he signed advanced bills of £100 for 'value secd. in mine' to be paid to William Harris Esq. on 31st December 1848 **Figure 3** and 31st December 1849.[14]

It is possible that Marshal Heath had leased further rights to the west of Higher Bowden and that these had lapsed at the end of 1847 and that Smith

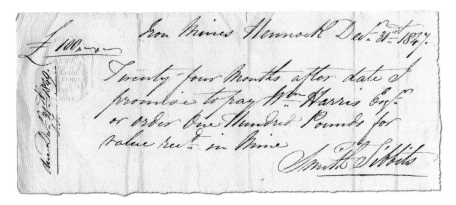

Figure 3 – Money Order from Smith Tibbits

Tibbits took them over. The location of the area leased is not known but it is reasonable to assume that this was in the area later occupied by the Shaptor, and Plumley mines.

The next mention we have is in August 1848 when the Mining Journal carried an advertisement for the **Hennock Iron Steel and Tin Mining Co**. This was a Cost Book company with a capital of £9450 in 4500 shares at £2 2s. each, the initial deposit was to be £1 1s per share.

> *The promoters of this company propose to raise the above capital to work efficiently the very valuable mines of micaceous iron ore and tin ore situate in the parish of Hennock.*
>
> *These mines are not a new discovery, but possess the advantage of having had their merits tested to an extent that fully establishes their great capabilities and warrant the expectation of large trade at a highly remunerative profit.*
>
> *The sett about a mile long from east to west and half a mile wide....nearly the whole feature of which is a decomposed granite said to be highly productive in metalliferous deposits particularly having an unlimited quantity of rich micaceous peroxide of iron yielding 50 per cent of iron, of a very superior quality for the manufacture of steel. A lease is held for 21 years at a standard rent of £3000 without other dues. From one lode averaging 7 feet. wide at a depth of 10 fathoms. 16,000 tons of this iron ore have been raised, and can be continued, at a cost not exceeding 2/- per ton and it is estimated that 2000 tons per month may be disposed of yielding a profit of from £4000 to £5000 per year. The Bovey lignite is in*

the immediate vicinity and may hereafter prove highly valuable for smelting purposes. Tin has been found in a distinct lode from the above.[15]

As the sett was described, it included just about everything from Great Rock to Plumley. The description of iron production from a depth of 10 fathoms indicates that this was probably referring to the mines leased by Tibbits. Whether anything came of this proposal is not known.

A fresh operation under the title **Hennock Iron Mines** was started in October 1853 when George Perriman[c] leased: Challacombe (Chericombe) Head Field, Challacombe Head Long field, The Mow Field, Three Corners, Ten Acres, The Eight Acres, Shapter Longfield and Shapter Park all part of Higher Bowden Estate to James Newall, John Francis Ford and Capt. John Burgan for £75 for the first year and £100 per year thereafter. **Hennock Iron Mines** does not seem to have much of a success for in June 1854 the Secretary to the company (J A Gordon) was instructed to sell as one adventurer refused to pay calls.[16] In June the mine's auction was advertised:

Valuable Iron Mines with Machinery near Newton Abbot.

*Mr C Warton is directed to sell by auction at the mart on Friday 16th June at Twelve for One o'clock precisely pursuant to the resolution of the shareholders, the **Hennock Iron Mine** desirably situate at Hennock near Bovey Tracy and Newton, in the County of Devon, including the valuable sets of grants, of which there are 20 years unexpired, together with the MACHINERY, TOOLS etc. also 300 tons of ore at Teigngrace canal. The mine is now in a state of readiness for immediate development to any extent, and has every symptom of a successful venture.*[17] (The Mart was in London)

Whether the mine was sold as a going concern is not known, but a Capt. Rogers was appointed the superintendent of the iron mines at Hennock in February 1855.[18]

Another operation started at this time was the **Hennock Black Ore Mining Co Ltd** where work began in 1856.[19] the manager being H Rickard. By early 1857 the Mining Journal reported

Since our having commenced operations we have laid open a consider-able length of lode. We have made our dressing floors and put in dressing

---

[c] In the 1851 census Perriman is described as a farmer of 123 acres employing one labourer, he must, there-for have let out much of his land. At that time he was a widower living in Hennock village.

apparatus for cleaning 15 tons per month.....roads to dressing floors and an ore shed for drying, 8 tons ready for market.[20]

The small monthly tonnage and the reference to dressing and drying indicates that this mine was probably producing micaceous haematite rather than ordinary iron ore. Could this have been Great Rock?

In July 1857 in an account of iron mines of Dartmoor[21] there is reference to the production of some black ore and shining ore from **Hennock** and shining ore from **Beadon** and **Kelly**. As we have seen, Hennock could be just about anywhere but might be Great Rock. Beadon (presuming that it was not a corruption of Bowden) is more specific. It is possibly referring to workings of the western part of Great Rock mine which is bounded on the west by Beadon Lane and to the north by the Beadon Brook or perhaps an eastern extension of the Bowden Hill mine.

During 1858 trials for smelting micaceous haematite were made at Rhymney, S Wales but apparently they were not successful.[22]

Not withstanding this, the following information was published about the same time regarding the **Hercules Mine** on a site of 100 acres with a 21 year lease. As part of a call for funds, it was stated that the mine had been proved for 400 fathoms at great cost and about 180,000 tons of crystalline haematite (specular iron) had been laid open above adit as well as large quantities of shining ore *"in great demand as a lubricant in combination with grease"*. Several thousand tons of shining ore had been sold for £3/ton.[23] This description tallies with the Bowden Hill mine area.

Iron Ore from **Hercules** *gave 94.25 per cent of peroxide of iron as analysed by Mr Joe Mitchell of London*[24]

The mine was operated by the **South Devon Iron & General Mining Co.** who were also involved in the **Atlas and Phoenix** mines.

In the middle of 1859 it was reported that:

A small high pressure engine has been erected on this mine which readily keeps it in order by working 8 hours per day....we have a good course of iron ore there, about 4ft. wide, producing 13 tons/fathom worth 17/- per ton. The striking feature of the iron lode in this mine is its great regularity, scarcely varying a degree in its bearing or underlie and equally little in width. There has been laid open a course of iron of upwards of 300 fms in length. We shall continue our levels with all speed and also with the sinking of the engine shaft.[25]

Operations did not last long as Hercules was abandoned in December 1860.[26]

South Devon Iron and General Mining Company were in the news again in June 1861 when it was announced that they were to commence the erection of a furnace to smelt iron from **Atlas** using the local lignite as a fuel,[27] the work being superintended by Mr S B Rogers.[28] The project was abandoned in February 1862.[29]

Also in 1862 there was an advertisements for the **Hennock Copper Tin and Iron Lodes**:

> *To be let for a term of 7, 14 or 21 years from Lady-day last, all these iron lodes with indications of copper and tin lodes on part of Higher Bowden Estate, Mr George Perriman, Hennock Village, Devon.*[30]

This was followed by a further advertisement in October 1864

> *Iron ore in and under an extensive tract in Hennock near Chudleigh offered for sale. Apply to Henry Gibson of Haldon Hall or Capt Nicholls of South Exmouth.*

In April 1866 it was offered again but nothing much appears to have been done and the flotation appears to have been a failure.[31] No indication is given as to where this was but the Haldon Estate owned some of the Great Rock mineral rights.

Shortly afterwards, in December 1866, Capt. James Seccombe wrote a report on the **Hennock Iron Mine** for a Mr Henry Blatchford:

> *Sir – Agreeably with your request I have made an inspection of the **Hennock Iron Mine**, and beg to hand you the following report thereon.*

> *This sett is situated in the well known iron bearing ground to the north of Bovey Tracey, and has running through the entire length a large course. The former proprietors worked on the back of this for a considerable extent and sold therefrom an immense quantity of iron of a very high percentage and I learn notwithstanding their having to cart their ore to Newton and forward it thence by boat to Teignmouth for shipment, they derived great profit therefrom. Having continued their operations as deep as the water would permit of they brought up a lobby from the lowest part of the sett and commenced an adit which after having driven a few fathoms was abandoned (probably in consequence of a depression in the trade at that time and the great expense of carriage) before the run of ores*

was reached. Since that time a Railway has been opened from Newton to Mortonhampstead, passing within a very short distance of this property, by which the iron can be taken at a small cost direct to Teignmouth, thereby saving sufficient in cartage and haulage alone to leave a good profit.

Judging from the size and character and productivity of the lode where opened upon at the surface. I see no reason for doubting the statements made as to the former workings, nor that returns equal to anything previously done can be made – if not far exceeded. To do this it will be necessary to open and drive up the adit level, which course I recommended being adopted, by so doing you will be enabled to work without machinery, as it will both drain off the water and act as an outlet for the ores, thereby saving the waste and damage of land and the cost of pumping which open working, as previously adopted would entail.

After making careful enquiries of those who were engaged in the late working and who now have no interest whatever in it, and comparing their statements with what I have been enabled to see for myself I have arrived at the conclusion that a capital of £1500 will be ample to drive up the adit and bring ore to market, and that when laid open returns of from 4000 to 6000 tons of iron a year may be calculated upon, at a profit at the lowest calculation of 3/- to 4/- per ton.[32]

Almost certainly this is Perriman's Bowden Hill mine. There are records of a crosscut adit started from the valley, about 300 yards N.W. of Chericombe Head, that was driven 80 fms south into the mine.[33]
Dines writing in 1956[34] states

An iron lode (erroneously indicated as a tin lode in the 1-inch geological map of 1913) can be traced by a line of old surface workings commencing near the road, 350 yds. southeast of Beadon Cross and extending 600 yds. east 15 degrees north; the underlie is northward. The mine is said to have been first opened in 1873 by an adit driven from the valley, about 300 yds NW of Chericombe Head, for 80 fms. as a crosscut and for 100 fms. W along the lode. Later Engine shaft was sunk vertically to 23 fms. below the adit (13 fms.) and levels driven east and west at 6.5, 10, 16.5 and 23 fms. below adit; none of which exceeds 15 fms. in length. **Figure 4** *A small amount of stoping was done from above adit level to the 16.5 fm. level. A second lode, 10 fms. south was picked up in crosscuts at adit and at the 16.5 fm levels but the amount of driving done on it was small.*

The exact location of the shaft is not known but it is presumably situated somewhere along the old openworks. No records of output.

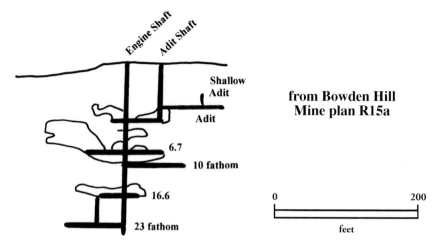

from Bowden Hill
Mine plan R15a

Figure 4 – Section through Bowden Hill Mine

Our last reference to the **Hennock Iron Mine** is around 1870 when the mine was acquired by the Van Iron Ore Company where Capt W H Hosking was manager during the period 1870-73 (181 tons sold in 1872 for £60). We will hear more of William Hosking in the next chapter.

Richard Meade, then Assistant Keeper of Mining Records in London writing in the Mining Journal in 1877 about iron mining in Devon said:

> *Of the ores raised from the mines of Brixham one kind – a brilliant micaceous haematite of a soft variety – is prepared and ground in a mill with linseed oil into paint which is largely employed in the coating of ironwork and is usually known as Torbay paint..... These Torbay paints are advantageously used in preventing and arresting rust.....and are used by gas and railway companies and various departments of the Government.*

There were two competing paint companies at Brixham, Both produced oxide-based paints. Their red-oxide paints were well known for use on iron structures. The reference to brilliant micaceous haematite is very specific yet there are no references to micaceous haematite being produced from the Brixham mines.[35] Either Meade has got this wrong or perhaps he is referring to paints made in Brixham from Hennock material. He goes on :

Brown iron ore also occurs at Hennock, in an east and west lode, and has been worked at intervals over a distance of nearly two miles and to the depth from 20 to 30 feet and is said to have gone down very rich, the ore being of a micaceous character yielding 55 per cent metallic iron, the lode nearly vertical and about 4 feet wide, being worked by two adits driven on the lode from the bottom of the hill. In 1872 from a return of that year there appears to been 181 tons raised from the Hennock district.[36]

The question is which hill? This could be Kelly or Great Rock. Whilst so far there has not been any reference that can clearly be attributed to Great Rock, the 1888 O.S. map of the area shows an air shaft and another shaft labelled "old" in the area that was to become the present mine area.

Despite the many references to iron mining in the Hennock area, no production figures appear in the Mining Records until 1879. This is surprising when we know that Richard Meade was one of the original 'Clerks of the Mineral Statistics' who were responsible for producing the official records.

Richard Meade had joined Robert Hunt, Keeper of the Mining Records, in the original Mining Record Office in 1841, retiring in 1889. The keeping of mining records was started in the mid-1840's by the Geological Survey and Museum. The first records were for copper and lead. Regular collection and publication of mineral extraction appeared in 1855 for the year 1853. This continued until 1882 when the Mining Record Office was transferred to the Home Office where the Mine Inspectors had for many years been publishing a similar range of output data in their annual reports. The Coal and Metalliferous Mines Regulations Acts of 1872 had required all mines to furnish the Inspectorate with details of their output and employment and it was thought wasteful to continue the collection of voluntary returns and computations of the Mining Record Office. With some changes this system continued up until 1914.[37]

An indication to the extent of iron mining in the area can be gained from the Census returns for 1881. At that time there were 11 iron miners living in Hennock, 4 in Bovey Tracey and 1 in Trusham. None were recorded in Lustleigh, Christow or Moretonhampstead. We know from the Mineral Statistics that 3 men were employed at Kelly, but where were the rest of them working?

Finally, John Harris writing to the Western Morning News newspaper in January 1897 tells us that old workings and refuse heaps can be seen

.....in plain view of the main road on the North Combe and Shaptor estates, where the largest of the present mines are situated, and from

some of which ore was taken longer ago than I can remember – certainly 40 years.

The North Combe and Shaptor workings referred to here are probably those which were later worked and known as the Plumley and the Shaptor mines. These are covered further in the next chapter.

To sum up, we know that by 1880, mining had taken place at Kelly, Shaptor and North Combe, Bowden Hill and one or more 'Hennock' mines. We know that some mining had taken place at Great Rock as the First Edition Ordnance Survey Map of 1889 shows an 'air shaft' and 'old shaft' on the site. Additionally some work had been done at Shuttamoor as the 1889 O.S. map shows an 'old shaft'.

1. Cecil Torr was a barrister-at-law and lived at Yonder Wreyland in Lustleigh – coincidentally this was close to the house 'Yonder Wrayland' owned by the family of Tony Haydon-Baillie (see later) with whom the author stayed when, as a student, he worked at Great Rock.
2. Cecil Torr, the Wreyland Documents, Cambridge University Press, 1910, p.xxxiv.
3. Roberts P., KMPS Newsletter, February 1997.
4. Svedentierna Eric, Tour of Great Britain, 1802-3.
5. Lysons, Devonshire, (1812), p.cclxviii.
6. De la Beche, Report on the Geology of Cornwall, Devon & West Somerset, 1839, p6.
7. Hamilton Jenkin A. K., Mines of Devon - North and East Dartmoor, Devon Library Services, 1981. p145-151.
8. Brooke notes. Notes on mines in Devon and Cornwall collected by Justin Brooke of Marazion.
9. Mining Journal, 17 April 1841, p121.
10. Devon Record Office, Exeter, Tithe Redemption Map, 1841.
11 Information for this section is derived from documents referring to this case in the DRO at Exeter 924 M/B.2/26 and from Justin Brooke's extensive notes.
12. Mining Journal, 25 May 1844, p178.
13. 947 M/L.46/4, DRO Exeter.
14. Copy of Money orders dated 31 December 147, courtesy of Greg Ramstedt, descendant of William Harris.
15. Mining Journal, 4th August 1848, p365.
16. 947 M/L.46, DRO Exeter.
17. Mining Journal, 10th June 1854, p387 - Auction Notice.
18. Mining Journal, 17 February 1855, p.105.
19. Brooke notes.

20. Mining Journal, 14 February 1857, p114.
21. Brooke notes.
22. Atkinson M, unpublished PhD thesis "Iron Ore Mining in Mainland Britain..." University of Exeter 1981, p132.
23. Brooke notes.
24. Mining Journal, 16 April 1859, p268.
25. Mining Journal, 30 July 1859, p531.
26. Mining Journal, 8 December 1860.
27. Mining journal 29 June 861 p451
28. Mining Journal, 28 September 1861, p627
29. Mining Journal, 22 February 1862.
30. Mining Journal, 2 Aprii 1862, p.286, and 17 May 1862, p337.
31. Brooke notes.
32. Trevithick Society Newsletter, No. 15, November 1976. Letter dated 31 December 1866.
33. Dines H G, The Metalliferous Mining Region of South-West England, HMSO, 1956 p.726.
34. Dines H. G., The Metalliferous Mining Region of South West England, HMSO, 1956, p726.
35. Doug Westaway pers. com. 7 August 2002
36. Mining Journal, 30 June 1877, p711 - (Supplement).
37. Burt R. et al, Cornish Mines, Metalliferous and Associated Minerals 1845-1913, University of Exeter, 1987, p viii-ix.

CHAPTER TWO

THE DEVELOPMENT YEARS 1877-1900

Whilst Great Rock only started, or more correctly re-started about 1895, it was the re-starting of the Kelly Mine around 1877, that was to mark the beginning of a continuous period of micaceous haematite production in Devon that only ceased in 1969. Two men will forever be associated with this period of mining in South Devon, namely W.H.Hosking and E.M.Slatter.

William Henry Hosking was an interesting character. He was born in 1839 at Lydford, West Devon. It is not known where he was educated or whether he had any formal training in mining and the management of mines. In any event by the age of 21 he was in the Ashburton area where he was the chief agent both for the Sigford Consols Copper Mine and the Smith's Wood Mine. These were small operations, little more than prospects and his involvement with them lasted only two years. Over the next 15 years he was involved in over two dozen local mines including four for the Van Iron Ore Company. As well as his involvements in Devon and Cornwall. Hosking also worked iron mines in Eskdale in Cumbria. (**Appendix I**)

This must be the classic example of 'get a man with a full diary'. In reality his involvement with these mines would have been more that of a consulting engineer keeping a general eye on progress. If you wanted to open an iron mine in the West Country then William Hosking was your man.

Kelly mine was reopened by the Kelly Iron Company and William Hosking was employed as the Chief Agent. Two years later, in the Mineral Statistics for 1879, he is recorded as being the owner. In 1880 the ownership is recorded to have passed to the Kelly Iron Mines Company only to revert back to Hosking in 1882. Confusingly, Kelly's Directory for Bovey Tracey, 1885[1], states that the mine was still owned by the Kelly Iron Mines Co. with W.H.Hosking acting as their agent. Despite the grand name it was a tiny operation producing some 20 to 30 tons of micaceous haematite per year and only employing two or three people. Kelly continued to be worked in this small way by Hosking until 1891 but the mine cannot have occupied much of his time.

It is possible that Hosking, as well as being the agent, was also major shareholder in, or perhaps owned, the companies reported above, and that the variations in ownership reported are purely differences in the way that he completed official returns which tend to be completed quickly, even today. I suspect that Hosking was no exception and this is evidenced by the production figures that have been very much rounded up - or even made up. It is highly unlikely that a mine like this would have produced exactly 20 tons per year for three consecutive years.

Kelly Mine Production 1879 - 1891

1879	20 tons	1886	22 tons
1880	22 tons	1887	30 tons
1881	25 tons	1888	25 tons
1882	30 tons	1889	30 tons
1883	20 tons	1890	30 tons
1884	20 tons	1891	30 tons
1885	20 tons		

Hosking's involvement with Kelly ceased in 1892 when the mine closed. Some 10 years later, in 1901, the mine was reopened by the Scottish Silvoid Company. They operated the mine until it was taken over by the Ferrubron Manufacturing Company - but we anticipate.

The other man, perhaps **the** man, who was responsible for the success of the micaceous haematite mining in Devon, was E.M. Slatter. Edmund Meek Slatter was born in Africa, probably in 1858. He is given as being aged 25 on his marriage certificate of 21st February 1884 which indicates a birth date of either 1858 or 1859. This is contradicted by his death certificate of 19th December 1933 when his age was given as 77 years implying a birth date of 1856. To add the confusion he is given as 76 on his gravestone which gives his birth year as 1857. I believe the marriage certificate to be the most reliable as he must have been there at the time! His father was stated to be a 'newspaper proprietor' in Pietermaritzburg in the British Colony of Natal, in what is now South Africa. Edmund Slatter arrived in Devon probably about 1882. Norman Bennett,[a] who knew Slatter, tells us that Slatter had successfully prospected for, and mined in a small way, gold and diamonds, and had decided to retire to his native Devon.[2] For a man who was in his mid-20's the word retirement is perhaps misleading. More likely he made or inherited money and decided to settle in England.

So what kind of a world did Slatter come from? Britain's involvement in South Africa started in 1806 when the British Government took possession

---

[a] Norman Bennett, a chemist, started work for the paint manufacturer, Griffiths Bros, in the early 1920's. He later became a director. Griffiths Bros. eventually had a controlling interest in the Ferrubron Manufacturing Co. that owned Great Rock.

of what was then known as the Cape Colony. This was done mainly for strategic reasons as the Cape provided a key naval base on the route to India. In 1834 Britain ordered slaves to be emancipated and this precipitated the 'Great Trek' when many of the resident Boers, or poorer Afrikaners, some of whose roots went back to immigration from Holland in the 1600's, moved northeast out of the colony.

For the next sixty years the British Government blew hot and cold in its dealings with the Boers. In 1843 Britain created a second colony by annexing Natal, one of the areas in which the Boers had settled. This could have been the time that Slatter's father moved to Natal. Edmund Slatter would have been born and brought up as a privileged English speaking white in the British colony. Later, in 1852, Britain recognised the independence of the Boer state of Transvaal which lay to the north of Natal.

In April 1877 Britain annexed the Transvaal as the first step in an attempt to federate South Africa. At this time Slatter would have been 19 and if in fact he did go into prospecting and mining then this would have been about the time when he started. At that time gold was being principally worked in the Eastern Transvaal and diamonds had been discovered at Kimberley on the border between Cape Province and the Boer Orange Free State. The annexation of the Transvaal was reversed in 1881 after Paul Kruger had led a rebellion culminating, on the 27th February 1881, in the defeat of the British at Majuba.[3]

Shortly after this Slatter must have left for England as we know that on the 21st of February 1884 he was married to twenty-one year old Catherine Shapley at St. Marks Church, Torwood, Torquay.[4] Edmund Slatter was then described as a 'landowner'. Catherine Shapley was one of several children of the well-known grocer and wine merchant, Edward Shapley, who is shown in the 1881 census as employing 25 men and 3 boys. From the Marriage Certificate it would also appear that the young Slatter was staying, or lodging, in Torquay at the Shapley family home of 'Hatton'. It is not known how and when Edmund met Catherine, but short engagements were unusual so we can assume that he had been in Devon for a couple of years.

The 1881 Census[5] shows that Catherine, then 18 years old, was one of six children and was working as a governess. Doubtless she was employed in caring for the children of one of the wealthy families who, at that time, lived in Torquay. The Census fails to record an Edmund Slatter in Devon at this date so we may assume that he had not yet arrived in England.

Sometime around the time of his marriage Slatter purchased the small Hawkmoor estate, presumably using the money that he had 'earned' in South Africa. The estate lay to the east of the road from Bovey Tracey to Moretonhampstead. It is not known exactly when he purchased the estate -

was ownership of the estate the reason why he described himself as a landowner on his marriage certificate? However, the first documentary evidence of the Slatter's presence at Hawkmoor is some four years later when Kelly's Directory of 1888/9 records Edmund Slatter as a farmer and the owner of 'Hawkmoor'. Slatter told Norman Bennett that when he took possession of Hawkmoor the agent said:

Well, Mr Slatter I have charged you for everything on the property except the shining stuff in the ground.[6]

Returning to Slatter's domestic arrangements, the 1891 Census,[7] found that the Slatter family had 'slept away' on Sunday night. A further examination shows that Edmund, his wife Catherine, his mother Elizabeth Slatter and two servants were staying with his in-laws, the Shapleys, at Torquay. Here is given the first evidence to support Edmund's South African origins; his place of birth being given as Pietermaritzburg, Africa.[8]

The 'shining stuff' must have made Hawkmoor particularly attractive to Slatter where he could have his own mine almost literally in his own back garden. Interest in the shining stuff was to dominate the Slatters' lives for the next 40 years. We are told that

in a short time he was extracting and refining, probably with no more elaborate equipment than a vanning shovel, small quantities of the mineral we know as micaceous haematite.[9]

Whether he actually did this is not proven, but we know that by 1892 he was the owner of the Shaptor mine (SX 806810) which lay just across the shallow valley to the south of Hawkmoor House. The mine was worked on a larger scale than Kelly which had then just closed. During Slatter's ownership, which lasted until 1901, the mine employed, along with Shuttamoor (see later), about 12 people and produced some 80 tons per year of paint grade micaceous haematite. There is no record in the official statistics as to who was the manager or agent during this period and it is tempting to guess that Hosking, with his considerable local experience, was involved.

In October 1892, the lease of the North Coombe Mine, was taken over by James Dick of R.&J.Dick Gutta Percha Merchants of Glasgow.[10] Why Scottish companies should be interested in micaceous haematite both here and later at Kelly is not clear. North Coombe, just down the valley from Shaptor, was known later as the Plumley mine (SX 804806). There are indications that the previous lessees had done some work here as the 1888

Ordnance Survey map shows a building where the remains of the Plumley dressing floors can now be found. This was a separate operation from Slatter's Shaptor as Plumley had its own dressing plant downstream from the Shaptor plant. The Chief Agent was a Mr Alexander Livingstone[b] (Plate 1) who does not appear to have been involved in any of the other micaceous haematite mines in the area.

Plate 1. Alexander Livingstone and his family picnic at Shaptor Rock about 1896 (KMPS collection)

In 1893 there was a dispute between the lessees of Plumley and E.M.Slatter over the use of the water in the stream. This dispute threatened the working of Plumley as:

...my wheel and stamps are almost complete and we hope to get a lot of ore dealt with immediately.[11]

First recorded production from Plumley was in 1896. The mine employed 6-8 men half of whom worked underground.

---

[b] Alexander Livingstone died on the 17th December 1897, aged 40. His wife Margaret gave birth to their seventh child, Alexandrina, in 1898.

At the same time that Slatter was busying himself with Shaptor, Otto Schmidt^c & Co were opening, or possibly re-opening, the Hawkmoor mine (SX 798818) with the inevitable William Hosking as the Chief Agent. Where the name of the mine came from is not known, as the mine is some two-thirds of a mile north-west of the site of Hawkmoor house and a few hundred yards east of Kelly mine. The mine was another of these tiny operations and only employed 6 men at most and more normally two or three. The production figures up to 1897 include the larger output from Shaptor. Thereafter the mines' production statistics are reported separately with Hawkmoor's output running at some 40 tons per year.

We get a glimpse of the industry in 1895 when Joseph Martin, HM Inspector of Mines, wrote[12]

The mineral herewith exhibited by consent of Mr W.H.Hosking is from the Hawkmoor and Shaptor Mines, at Lustleigh, near Bovey Tracey, Devonshire. It is a micaceous iron ore, commonly known as shining ore, and is used mainly for making paint. It exists in the granite formations, in lodes holding an east and west direction, and underlying north. The lodes are small, ranging from two feet to two inches in width.

The present sample of the ore is as prepared for sale. It is sometimes found quite soft and fine, like the sample, and only requires washing to take out the little sand that is in it. On the average, however, quite 50 per cent of the ore stuff is massive and stony, and requires to be stamped and washed.

The granite in which the ore is found is that of the eastern fringe of the Dartmoor range, and Mr Hosking has not any doubt that its lodes are the same as those which carry tin and have been worked for tin further west, in and near the centre of the range; indeed, he has found one very good patch of tin ground in one of the shining ore mines.

The ore has been used for smelting into metallic iron. Several cargoes of it were shipped to Wales for that purpose about 25 years ago, but, generally speaking, the lodes were too narrow to yield a paying quantity, even then when the price was very high. Now, at the present price, it is entirely out of the question.

For paint purposes the demand is limited, and so also the mining operations, which consist of a few adits or levels driven into the hill sides.

^c Otto Schmidt was born in Russia and was a naturalised British Subject. In 1901 he was aged 45, living in Lewisham, London and was described as a 'Merchant Chemical & Mineral'

A full chemical analysis of the ore, carried out by Sheraton Cowper-Coles, can be found in **Appendix II**.

Meanwhile, Otto Schmidt & Co. did not stop at Hawkmoor and in 1896 were showing interest in the Great Rock Mine where 4 men were employed underground and William Hosking was the Chief Agent. No production appears to have resulted from this work and we have to wait until 1902 before the mine was brought into production.

There must have been something of a mini-mining boom in the Hennock area at this time for Slatter, wishing to increase production, re-opened the Shuttamoor mine (SX 823829). Some previous working is evidenced by an 'old shaft' marked on the First Edition Ordnance Survey map. For this re-working we have no separate statistics for the mine as they were reported with Shaptor. Whoever completed the official returns seems to have had trouble spelling the name of the mine as it is variously reported as Shuttamoor, Shoutamoor and Shortamoor.

At the end of the century, Kelly is closed, G Gartzke & Co. had taken over the interests of Otto Schmidt & Co.[d] in Great Rock and Hawkmoor, Slatter is working Shaptor and Shuttamoor and Dick is working Plumley.

[d] G.Gartzke & Co. remain something of a mystery. There remains a strong tradition in the Hennock area of German involvement in the early years of the industry. J Brooke notes.

Production of Micaceous Haematite 1892-1913 (tons)

From Atkinson et al – Dartmoor Mines – The Mines of the Granite Mass, 1978.

	Great Rock	Kelly	Hawkmoor	Plumley	Shaptor and Shuttamoor	Total
1892			36		48	84
1893			60		50	110
1894			*		*	230
1895			*		*	230
1896			*	*	*	273
1897			*	*	*	194
1898			60	54	74	188
1899			40	50	90	180
1900			40	50	88	178
1901		20	40	75	90	225
1902	87	80	10	15	20	212
1903	100	50		3	40	193
1904	100	122		60	40	322
1905	100	180		75	60	415
1906	142	160		60	74	436
1907	120	202		50	60	432

	Great Rock	Kelly	Hawkmoor	Plumley	Shaptor and Shuttamoor	Total
1908	122	70		80	55	327
1909	162	197		47	51	457
1910	140	185		50	20	395
1911	205	88		26	53	372
1912	266	165				431
1913	350	170				520

Notes: Mines marked * produced but an aggregate only was given.
For 1892-7 figures for Shaptor and Shuttamoor are for Shaptor only.

From Atkinson M et al – Dartmoor Mines – The Mines of the Granite Mass, 1978.

1. KMPS September 1995 and February 1997 have extensive notes on W H Hosking.
2. Norman Bennett in a letter to D.M.Bishop February 1980 – copy in author's files.
3. Pakenham T., The Boer War, Weidenfeld & Nicholson Ltd, 1979.
4. Marriage Certificate of E.M. Slatter/C.T.A. Shapley, 1884.
5. The 1881 National Census, Torquay.
6. Bennett to Bishop, February 1980.
7. The 1891 National Census – Bovey Tracey.
8. This early period of Slatter's life in Devon was researched by Mr. Donald Rowlet of Watcombe, Torquay and published in the KMPS Newsletter of July 1999.
9. Bennett to Bishop, February 1980.
10. Letters in the Ramstedt collection in KMPS archives.
11. Letter from A.Livingstone to A.Harris, dated 11th January, 1893. G Ramstedt collection.
12. Martin Joseph S., Micaceous Iron Ore Near Bovey Tracey, Trans. Manchester Geological Soc. Vol.23 (1895), p162-3.

CHAPTER THREE

CONSOLIDATION 1900-1919

I n 1900, both Great Rock and Hawkmoor came into the ownership of G Gartzke and Company. Little mining was being done by the company as Great Rock was stopped and Hawkmoor ceased production in 1901. It is quite possible that Slatter had an interest in this company for shortly afterwards, in 1902, the ownership of Great Rock and Hawkmoor along with Slatter's Shaptor and Shuttamoor were transferred to the newly formed Ferrubron Manufacturing Company. In 1901, Slatter, who was still living at Hawkmoor House, now listed his profession as a 'Miner of Oxide of Iron' and his employment status was described as 'Employer working at home' [1]

Edmund Slatter, probably as a result of his efforts to market his micaceous haematite, had come to know J Russell Thornbery[a] of the paint manufacturers, Griffiths Bros. & Co.. Apparently he had told Thornbery of the potential of micaceous iron oxide (MIO) paint, particularly for the protection of iron and steel.[2] In 1902, the Ferrubron Manufacturing Co. Ltd. was formed in which Slatter was the major and Griffiths Bros. and Co. the principal minor shareholders. This is a classic example of vertical integration where the major consumer, Griffiths Bros, had some control over the supply of its raw materials. Despite its name, Ferrubron Manufacturing Company was only involved in the mining of micaceous haematite, selling its product to Griffiths and other paint manufacturers.

On amalgamation the focus of operations was moved from Shaptor and Shuttamoor, where production was reduced, to Great Rock where production was built up. No doubt Slatter moved some of his experienced men to the new development at Great Rock under the watchful eye of William Hosking, who remained as Chief Agent.

The turn of the century also saw the Scottish Silvoid Company re-open the Kelly mine which had been closed since 1891. Production was rapidly expanded here during the following years, reaching 180 tons per annum by 1905. Whether Scottish Silvoid manufactured MIO paint in competition with Griffiths Bros. is not known.

---

[a] Chairman of Griffiths Bros. and one time President of the Paint and Varnish Society (now merged into the Oil and Colour Chemists Association)

We do not know how much Slatter invested in his mining ventures but it must have been a considerable amount. It is possible that he overstretched himself financially and could not sustain both his estate and the mines as, at some point, the Slatters moved to a house in Chudleigh called Strathmore.[3] In any event he left Hawkmoor House some time around 1907 when an advertisement in a local newspaper offered the house for sale or for let. The Slatters certainly had lived on a grand scale. The property was described as consisting of four acres of grounds and gardens and the house comprising three reception rooms, eleven bedrooms, kitchen, bathroom, offices and a coach/motor house. In 1909 the estate was again advertised for let, prospective tenants were asked to contact Mr. James Stancombe at Plumley Mine for permission to view.[b] The little Plumley mine remained independent employing a few men until it was also taken over by Ferrubron in 1907, the ever present William Hosking being Secretary and Chief Agent. Plumley was run down and closed in 1911. In 1915 local newspaper articles describe the purchase of the entire Hawkmoor estate by Devon County Council and the commencement of construction of the Devon Sanatorium, which was to specialise in the treatment of tuberculosis. The remainder of the estate was divided into agricultural smallholdings.[4]

This is the appropriate moment to introduce the name Tucker which, along with Slatter and Hosking, runs like a thread through the history of these mines. We will start with Elias Tucker who, in 1876, was employed on surface at the Steeperton Tor mine.[5] The Steeperton Tor tin mine lies way out in the middle of North Dartmoor, some four and a half miles south-east of Okehampton. During March 1877 he spent 3 weeks working on the Deep Level. Later, in May, Elias was paid 5s. for *'watching at the Mine, Sundays'*. It is probable that during the time he, and some of the other men, lodged on the mine and was paid extra for not going home on the Sunday. Despite employing 27 men in 1878, the mine did not last long and was closed in 1879. The census of 1881 shows Elias Tucker, aged 37 and described as a copper miner. He was living at South Zeal with his wife Avis, their sons Elias - who I shall refer to as Elias (jnr) - aged 12, Charles George aged 7 and their daughter Sylvia aged 4. Elias (jnr) was born in the Warren House Inn[c] which was then kept by Elias's brother-in-law, the family then living in a bungalow just down the road from the inn. Elias was then probably working at the adjacent Golden Dagger or Vitifer Mines. Elias later moved with his family to Cumberland where he was engaged in the mining industry.[6] It is possible

[b] James Stancombe, known as 'Old' Jimmy Stancombe was born in Ashburton about 1849. In 1881 he was living at Haytor Vale and was probably working at Haytor Iron Mine. Shortly before 1901 he moved to Bovey Tracey. Both he and his son 'Young' Jimmy (aged 23) were described as 'Ore Miners' in the 1901 Census. 'Old' Jimmy Stancombe later became the general foreman at Kelly.

[c] The Warren House Inn, on the B3212 on the Two Bridges to Moretonhampsted road, still exists and serves a good pint. It is said that the fire in the bar is never allowed to go out.

that Elias went to work on one of the Eskdale iron mines managed by William Hosking.

It is not known when Elias Tucker came to work at Great Rock. The 1901 census shows both Elias (snr) and his son Charles to be living in Hennock and employed as 'Labourer Shining Ore Mining'. A photograph captioned 'Devonshire Mine at Trusham' **Plate 2**, printed in 1898, is thought to have been taken at Great Rock. It is obviously a newly opened or re-opened adit. It is believed that the man in the centre is Charles Tucker and to his left is Elias Tucker and 'Jack' Hosking, son of William Hosking.[7] It is not clear what role the goat played in the mining operation.

Plate 2 - 'Mine at Trusham' (Tucker collection)

It is known that Elias Tucker (jnr) worked in the gold mines near Madras. As he does not appear in the 1901 census we can assume that he was already in India. About 1902 Charlie went out to join him. **Plate 3**.

Charlie found that the climate in India did not suit him and he came back to Devon about 1907.[8] Elias (jnr) stayed on. **Plate 4**.

Plate 3 - Charlie Tucker and Elias Tucker (jnr) in India, about 1905 (© Tucker collection)

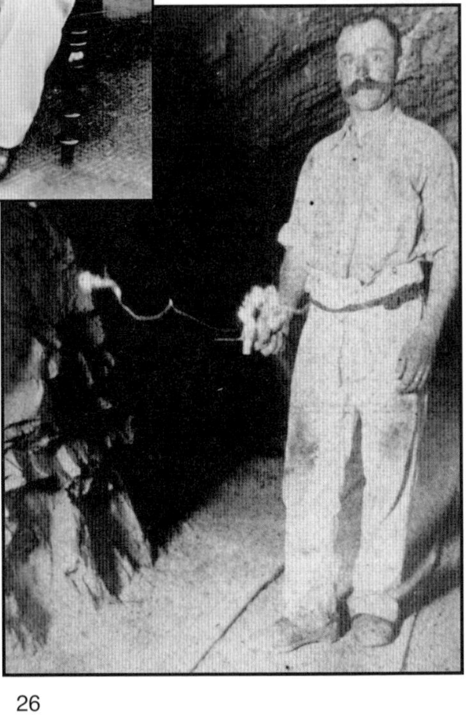

Plate 4 Elias Ticker (jnr) underground in India. Postcard dated 15th July 1905 (© Tucker collection)

On his return Charlie bought Union Cottage, next to the Palk Arms in Hennock, and we can assume that he then restarted work at Great Rock.

By 1910, Elias Tucker was working as foreman or chargehand between Great Rock and Shuttamoor. **Plate 5** shows the plant at Shuttamoor about this time.

Plate 5 - Shuttamoor dressing floors about 1908 (Chapman collection, Devon Record Office)

It is typical of the mills or washing plants of the period. On the left the ore is being washed and screened the undersize being fed to a washing strip. Larger pieces of ore were crushed in the small, waterwheel driven, Californian stamp battery before passing to another washing strip on the right of the picture. The overflow from the strips was then run into settling pits, dug out and dried for sale. The process is more fully described later in this chapter. The man with the beard by the stamps is probably Elias Tucker.

On February 11th 1911, Elias Tucker was killed when going to assist a trammer who was having difficulty in tipping an end tipping tub. Elias Tucker was a tall strong man. As he went to heave the tub forward the whole tub and chassis went over taking him with it, breaking his neck in the fall down the tip. He had not taken the usual precaution of hooking the chassis chain to the rail to prevent such a happening.[9] He was succeeded as Foreman at Great Rock by his son Charlie Tucker (later known as 'Old Man' Tucker to differentiate him from his son, also named Charlie, who was known as 'Young' Charlie).

Great Rock was developed by a series of adit levels driven westwards in from the hillside where the lodes outcropped at surface. A simple mill to process the mined ore **Plate 6** was erected in Lake's Copse, in a small valley just below the lowest level or No.3 level. This level was known to the miners as Sawbench Level.

Plate 6 - Great Rock dressing floors about 1902 (Chapman collection, Devon Record Office)

This location offered at least a limited supply of water for the mill. All ore haulage was either out of this lower level or by cart from the workings higher up where it could not be tipped down to the main level. The mill operated on similar lines to Shuttamoor. The piece of equipment on the left with the long handle is a jigging box - essentially a hand operated sieve moved up and down in a bath of water.

The final process of drying was located way down the valley on the bank of the Beadon Brook, not far from Hyner bridge. The haematite slurry travelled along a complex and lengthy system of wooden launders to the settling tanks. The reason for this location was probably because the mill site was too steep and restricted to permit the construction of the necessary settling tanks on one elevation. Another advantage of this location was that it was an easy haul to Trusham railway station. There is a similarity here with china clay working where the dries were often some distance from the pits.

T G Allen who worked at Great Rock after Shuttamoor closed recalled:

The staff of that day consisted of Capt. W Hosking, his son Capt Jack, Capt Slader (Slatter), Charlie Tucker - mine foreman, A Hellier, Jack Gloyn, John Chappel, Jim Stancombe (senior and junior), George Stancombe, Fred Gloyn, Ern Wills, Ern Sampson, Fred Counter, Ern Daw and Tom Allen.[10]

Production gradually picked up from 100 tons in 1903 to 350 tons in 1913 when the labour force had increased to 17. It remained at this level well into the 1920's.

Great Rock Production 1901 - 1913[11]

Year	Iron Ore Tons	Year	Iron Ore Tons
1901	nil	1908	122
1902	87	1909	162
1903	100	1910	140
1904	100	1911	205
1905	100	1912	266
1906	142	1913	350
1907	120		

Great Rock Labour - 1896 to 1926[12]

Year	Underground	Surface	Year	Underground	Surface
1896	4		1914	not available	
1901	2		1915	not available	
1902	4	3	1916	7	5
1903	4	4	1917	8	7
1904	6	3	1918	5	5
1905	4	3	1919	10	9
1906	4	2	1920	4	10
1907	4	4	1921	11	7
1908	4	2	1922	10	6
1909	4	2	1923	13	6
1910	5	3	1924	9	8
1911	4	5	1925	8	7
1912	6	8	1926	9	7
1913	6	11			

It was usual for over half of the men to work underground with the remainder employed on surface dressing operations. All but Great Rock and Kelly were closed by the beginning of the First World War. (**Table in Chapter 2**) Kelly mine was later taken over by Ferrubron giving the company a monopoly on the production of micaceous haematite in the U.K. By 1919 the labour force at Great Rock had reached an all time high of 19 and the mine had been extensively developed as Cantrill[13] describes:

The lode courses in a direction E 10 S, underlies to the north and ranges in thickness from 1.8 ins. to 5 ft.. There are four levels and several cross-cuts and winzes. The adit level is 1500 ft. long; the second level, 100 ft. above is also 1500 ft. long; the third 1100 ft. long, is 56 ft. above the second; whilst the fourth is 70 ft. above the third level, 130 ft. from surface, and 350 ft. long. After passing a set of 4-head Californian prospecting stamps, the crushed ore is carried in launders to sluice boxes and settling tanks. It is dug out of the latter, dried over kilns, and packed in casks in 8-10 cwt. parcels. The waterpower is derived from reservoirs working three water wheels. Compressed air is used for the drills. The ore is sold to manufacturers of non-corrosive paint, and to chemical works at Swansea and Cardiff.

Norman Bennett leaves us observations of what the mines were like in the early part of the 20th Century.

At the time of its formation, the Company possessed five mines in the southern foothills of Dartmoor around Bovey Tracey. Of these only two, Great Rock at Hennock and Kelly at Lustleigh, proved to have a reasonable life, and were the only ones in operation when the writer became acquainted with the pigment in 1920.

In contra distinction to the Austrian mineral, which is of such massive formation that it is mined by the room and pillar method, that in Devon was found in geological fractures and a lode of two feet was unusual.

All the lodes of MIO (micaceous iron oxide) to the south of Dartmoor (there has been a micaceous haematite mine to the north of Dartmoor at South Molton, but the mineral was not of pigment quality) ran in an east - west direction and have a hade[d] deviation from the vertical of 15 to 20 degrees.

[d] Hade is the angle between the lode and the vertical. Most mining people use the term 'dip' which is the angle between the lode and the horizontal. A hade of 10 degrees is the same as a dip of 80 degrees.

Because the lode width gave insufficient access and working space, blasting of the mineral face was a daily occurrence. The mining sequence started at the end of a week period when the miners ignited safety fuses as they left the work place and from a safe distance noted that all charges had exploded. By the next morning the work place was clear of fumes. The obvious gangue or addle from the 4-5 ft. advance. was trammed away to dump, while free and rock associated mineral was taken to refinery. When the work place had been cleared, drilling commenced and finally charges were placed and stemmed. The refinery feed consisted of soft free MIO, MIO entrapped in rock, china clay, addle and some iron pyrites (known to the miner as mundick).

Micaceous haematite from Kelly was generally of larger flake size, but of little or no greater thickness than that from Great Rock, and could be said to be superior. Kelly however was difficult to work and smaller than Great Rock, and changing economic factors brought about its closure in the 1940's.

In Devon the first refinery operation was to subject the crude product from the mine to water sprays which washed the gangue free of micaceous haematite and revealed rock associated mineral. Originally the mineral from the primary washing operation was fed into a trommel which graded the micaceous haematite bearing rock by size, and the sized heaps were shovelled into appropriate stamp tubs (or mortar boxes) *where the rock was cracked to release the micaceous haematite. The motive power for the trommel and stamps was provided by an 18 ft. overshot waterwheel, said to develop 6 H.P.*

The water borne unstamped or free run mineral in the trommel was subjected to the same treatment as was the output from the stamps but formed a different flow line. Both flows were fed into troughs (also known as strips or sluices) *provided with riffles or baffles set at about 3 ft. distances. Each trough was attended by a man with a long-handled shovel. He shovelled the heavy material building up behind the riffles back to the top of the trough until he considered it to be incapable of yielding more MIO when he put it into a tram for transport to the waste dump. The overflow from the trough was carried by pipes to settling tanks from which the pigment was dug out, dried in a coal fired flat-bed drier (essentially a heated hearth where the hot flue gases from a small furnace passed under floor on which the mineral was spread out to dry) and packed into 40 gallon casks. (barrels)*

The process although crude, was sound in principle in that it avoided unnecessary reduction in flake size, but it was inefficient from the view point of separating MIO from its contaminants and also from that of preventing the loss of good MIO to the waste dumps.

The most undesirable contaminant is pyrites. In the paint film it can oxidise to soluble sulphate and create corrosion centres. The presence of pyrites and its oxidation products is manifest in roseate spots in the paint film.

This method of concentration has much in common with the refining of china clay. The waste sand is settled and discarded first with the valuable mineral being contained in the overflow. Whilst the MIO has a high specific gravity, its particle size and shape causes it to remain in suspension. The methods as described here remained largely unchanged until after World War II.

1. 1901 Census
2. Letter from N.Bennett to Bishop 1980.
3. Interview - Ron Tucker 8th April 2002, author
4. KMPS February 1997. The research of this part of Slatter's life was undertaken by Mr. Donald Rowlet of Watcombe, Torquay.
5. Greeves T A P, Steeperton Tor Tin Mine, Dartmoor, Devon, Trans. Devon Ass. Advent. Sci.,1985 117, 101-127.
6. Ron Tucker in a letter to Bob Le Marchant, 25th January 2001.
7. Identified by Ron Tucker - April 2001
8. Interview - Ron Tucker 8th April 2002, author
9. Letter from Ron Tucker, Kelly Mine Preservation Society Newsletter, November 1997.
10. Transcript of an undated newspaper article (possibly 1960's) in KMPS archives
11. Devon & Somerset Mines, Mines Metalliferous and Associated Minerals 1845-1913, Burt R., 1987
12. 1896 - 1913 - Devon & Somerset Mines, Mines Metalliferous and Associated Minerals 1845-1913, Burt R., 1987. 1916 - 1925 pers. com. P H G Richardson of Totnes, 2nd June 1999.
13. Cantrill T.C. et al, Iron Ores of Devon & Cornwall, Mineral Resources Vol XIV p50-52, London HMSO, 1919.

CHAPTER FOUR

GREAT ROCK BETWEEN THE WARS

T he inter-war years were a period of steady expansion at the mine with
Old Man Tucker running the day-to-day affairs on the mine. One interesting snippet of information has come to light regarding some work done
by a local builder. Samuel Clark recorded:

> Mr E M Slatter, Great Rock Ennock (sic) Repairs to bedroom windows.
> Jan 9 1919[1]

It must have been to Slatter's house in Chudleigh or a temporary office or
building on the mine.

William Hosking died in 1925. He had retained an interest in the mine
well after retiring from any active involvement. One likes to think of these
two elderly men, Hosking and Slatter, who had known each other for over
30 years and who shared an enthusiasm for mining, sitting in the mine office
discussing future plans for the mine.

Some or all of the mineral rights in the Great Rock mining area were part
of the Haldon Estate, apparently owned or managed by the Commercial
Union Assurance Company. In May 1925 their local branch manager, Mr K
W C Middleton, wrote to his head office in London regarding the possible
sale of the mineral rights to Ferrubron:

> Haldon Estate, Great Rock Mine
>
> I beg to enclose herewith copy of a letter dated 14th instant received from
> Messrs. Ellis, Son and Bowden, also a copy of a letter dated 21st April
> last from the Chairman of the Ferrubron Manufacturing Co. Ltd., of
> London and one of 24th April addressed to Mr John F Bowden from Mr
> E M Slatter of Hennock, and you will note that a favourable offer of £325
> is made for the acquisition of mineral rights in connection with this
> mine. This offer appears to be very favourable, and I shall be glad to hear
> that you agree to Messrs. Ellis, Son & Bowden's recommendation.

I also enclose the bound records of the reservation of Minerals, Haldon Estate, and plan relating thereto, which kindly return when done with.[2]

1925 saw the first of several works outings organised by Slatter for the employees of the Ferrubron Manufacturing Company. This included the men from Kelly as well as Great Rock. The first trip was to take everyone to visit the British Empire Exhibition at Wembley. It took place one Saturday, and was so successful that they had a trip every year from then on. Places visited included Plymouth, Cheddar Caves, Weston-Super-Mare and Weymouth. Breakfast and dinner were ordered in advance. **Plate 7** shows one of these outings, date unknown. Charlie Tucker is standing front left holding a walking stick. Slatter clearly cared for his employees and, as a well travelled man, he no doubt recognised the advantages of broadening the outlook of his workers.[3]

Plate 7 – Ferrubon 'works outing', date unknown (© Tucker collection).

Great Rock seldom had a mention in the technical press. However, in 1927 there was enough of general interest to warrant a few lines in the Mining Journal when we are told that there was great activity in the Newton Abbot area, where mines working micaceous haematite were in full swing, the ore being used for paint making.[4] This was followed by the statement:

Bowder (sic) *mine and Great Rock mine are both producing vigorously, and there are several other small properties producing haematite in the parishes of Lustleigh and Hennock.*[5]

Bowder must be a corruption of Bowden, or Bowden Hill, where there was a brief unsuccessful attempt to re-work the mine for micaceous haematite. This is covered more fully in Chapter 14.

Three wooden bungalows were built on the mine in the 1920's. Two, on the track above the mine that leads to the present Great Rock Farm, were built to house mine employees.

Edmund Slatter built the first one for George Stancombe[a] who ran the drying sheds. It was called Springdale. The third bungalow (**Plate 8**) which doubled as the mine office was built about 1925 or 1926. Edmund Slatter had this built much in the style of a successful South African prospector.

Plate 8 – The mine bungalow and the washing plant about 1930 (© Tucker collection)

Ron Tucker recalls in an interview:

I was only a little tiny lad.....I went in the horse and trap with granddad (Old Man Tucker) *used to go to work then in a horse and trap.....they were also building the second bungalow up the top for Walt Webber.*

[a] George Stancombe was the younger brother of Jimmy Stancombe. He was, as we shall see later, 'young Charlie' Tucker's father-in-law.

Some firm from Bovey built it Coombes...carpenters, joiners and what not.

Edwin[b] Slatter **(Plate 9)** *lived in Chudleigh, my dad* (Young Charlie Tucker) *used to fetch him every day because they had a car* (the Tuckers also ran a taxi service in Hennock). *Used to come in fetch Edwin daily and take him to the mine.*

When the bungalow was finished, Mr and Mrs Slatter lived there but Mrs Slatter was too lonely and they went to live in the Osborne Hotel in Exeter, with short stays in the bungalow.

Plate 9 – Edmund Slatter clearing weed from one of the ponds by the drying sheds about 1930. (© Tucker collection)

In the early days the machinery was driven by water power. **(Plate 10)**

Whilst compressed-air powered rockdrills had been introduced, **(Plates 11, 12)** some of the rock drilling continued to be done by hand-drilling.

[b] Ron Tucker always refers to Edmund Slatter as Edwin.

Plate 10 – Washing plant wheel pre-1916. Old Man Tucker is on the right with Wills on his immediate left. One of the young lads is Sid Preston who we will meet later. (© Tucker Collection)

Plate 11 – Entrance to Sawbench or No.3 Level on South lode, late 1920's. L-R: Old Man Tucker, M. Gilliam, Young Charlie Tucker, ?, Bill Hine. Note the carbide lamp on the front of the wooden bodied wagon and the rock drill being carried by Bill Hine (© Tucker collection)

Plate 12 – The face on No.3 Level taken on the same day as Plate 11. Bill Hine is holding the drill while Young Charlie Tucker poses with a shovel. Note the candles in his breast pocket. (© Tucker collection).

Around 1930 an oil engine was added to run the compressor. Water power continued to be used to drive the rest of the machinery until the 1950's, when electricity was installed.

Bill Hine, who worked at the mine from 1917-1960, recalls that in the winter, when they were building up stocks for sales in the Spring and work would be slack, each man would take a cut in his wages – about 2/6d. to save a man being laid off.[6]

In the late 1920's the local haulage firm of W.S.Howard and Sons had the contract to transport the barrels of mineral from the drying sheds to Trusham station **Plate 13**. Note the barrels by the signal box.[c]

Tom Howard recalled:

We used to get 1/- a barrel to go up and pick them up and roll them on and truck 'em down to Trusham station.....We had to roll them from the lorry onto the truck and we had to up-end 'em....use to be two of us like and you had to catch 'em just right.[7]

---

[c] Trusham Station closed in the 1960's Today (2002) it is a very different picture. The road bridge is still in use and the main station building has been converted into a house. Surprisingly a corrugated clad shed with a curved roof has survived. Some of the platform is still visible, but everything else has gone or is hidden by trees and undergrowth.

Plate 13 – Trusham Station early in the 20th Century (Vic Michell, Middleton Press)

They got 3d. for each empty barrel brought back from the station. Their lorry at this time was a solid tyred Vulcan.

Archie Cudmore started on the mine about 1928, straight from Hennock School, aged about 14.[8]

> *We just left School – first job that was comin' up – 12/6 a week. 10 shillings for your board and half-a-crown for yourself. I went there as a grub boy as they called it, getting the dinners, running the messages and one thing and another. Part of the grub boy's job was to collect Mr Tucker's breakfast.... Mr Tucker did like a fried breakfast.... Mrs Tucker would have everything ready or nearly ready everything really hot....on a dish with a cover wrapped in a cloth in a wicker basket.... After about 12 months I suppose, I started washing the ore.*

> *Every morning I used to have to go from Great Rock to Beadon Bottom to open up the iron thing* (gate controlling flow of water into the launder)*....Every night about four, ten past four....Sid Preston would say to me go out to Beadon Bottom and shut the gate.* **Plate 14**

> *Mr Slatter lived in the bungalow, the manager was Old Mr Tucker – Charlie Tucker.... used to call him blowfly as he was always buzzing about.*

Plate 14 – Beadon Pond part-frozen, February 28th 1929. Young Charlie Tucker is standing on the left (© Tucker collection)

I spent quite a bit of time with an old boy called Harry Brock. Harry Brock was the general handyman. He, he was good, we used to do quite a bit in the wood clearing away trees and that.

The chap that used to drive the horses that I remember was a chap called Sid Heath. We lived, my mother and father, lived in the pub, not in the pub but next door to the pub in Union Cottage....they kept Union Cottage as a pub and it was called Union Inn....Well when you had a pub in those days it seemed natural to have stables. And the horse from the mine was stabled in our....and the chap who drove the horse lodged in our place. But whilst I was there the main thing happened they bought their first lorry, the mining company....they had a Ford Lorry. Naturally the boss's son (Young Charlie Tucker) *got the job as the lorry driver.*

Some pay sheets from the early 1930's have survived and from them we are told that in December 1932 W.Webber and G.Purdon were driving the top level North Lode on contract at a rate of £2 10s. per fathom. In the three weeks from November 14th to December 3rd 1932 they drove 5 fathoms. A year later in November 1933 W.James and E.Gardener were driving a new level on the Middle Lode for £2 5s.6d. per fathom. In January 1934 Old Man Tucker's wages were increased from £3 10s. per week to £5 per week and Young Charlie Tucker's from £2 2s.6d. per week to £3 10.0 per week. There was also an annual bonus paid to some employees for the year ending 31st December 1933.

1933 Annual Bonus

	£	s.	d		£	s.	d.
C Tucker	10	0	0	L Sampsom	6	8	4
C Tucker Jnr	6	5	10	W Wills	6	1	8
W Webber	6	7	6	M Pike	1	17	11
S Preston	6	5	0	W Pike	5	0	8

Old Man Tucker's wages fell again to £3 10s. per week in June 1934 after the interim period of £5 per week. There was also a general fall in the wages from this week. In September 1934 T.Avery and F.Hodges are recorded to have spent a week *working on launders* for which they were paid £2 8s. 9d. and £1 10s. 0d. respectively. In January 1933 there were 25 men on the mine all working a 6 day week.

Young Charlie Tucker, in the period 1929-31, used to drive the Great Rock lorry. It did work both for Great Rock and for Kelly taking materials to the mines, and collecting casks of ore for delivery to the railway stations. In 1931 Slatter bought a car and went to live permanently in Exeter. Young Charlie and his family also moved to Exeter and Young Charlie then became Slatter's chauffeur and used to drive him to and from Hennock every day. The lorry driving was taken by Arthur Winslade (a Bovey Tracey man).[9]

Edmund Meek Slatter died at his home, 13 Queens Terrace, Exeter, on the nineteenth of December 1933. Mrs A E Flewin, who was then a resident housekeeper with the Slatters, provided the information for the death certificate. He was buried in Bovey Tracey cemetery and his headstone reads:

In loving memory of Edmund M Slatter late of Hawkmoor died 19th Decr 1933 aged 76[d] – At Rest, Also of Catherine Thyrza Alice Slatter Wife of the Above Died 2nd July 1941 aged 79.

---

[d] His death certificate states his age as 77.

The Slatters had no children and, apart from a number of named bequests, Slatter left all of his estate in trust to his niece and three nephews, who still lived in Africa, on the basis that his wife had the benefit of the income from the estate during her lifetime. His estate was valued at £13,519, a not inconsiderable sum when a miner was earning about £150 per year. Included in the will were individual bequests to all of the employees at Great Rock and Kelly mines. Right to the end the mines must have meant a great deal to him and giving money to his workers was a fine gesture indeed. Top of the list of the 23 employees at Great Rock was 'Old Man' Tucker who received £50 followed by Young Charlie with £20 right down to Ernest Gardner who got two pounds and ten shillings. Slatter's interest in the mine must have been sold at this time and it is thought that it was acquired by Griffith's Bros. as from now on they controlled operations on the mines.

Sadly, three of the beneficiaries of Slatter's will were shortly to die as a result of their employment in mining. The Cornish Post and Mining News reported in December of 1935:

> *3 men who worked in Great Rock Iron Oxide Mine at Hennock died of silicosis, it was stated at an inquest at Newton Abbot. A verdict was returned, in accordance with the medical evidence, the jury adding the rider that every known precaution was taken by the employers. They were Walter Lionel Webber 38, Albert Henry Cudmore 55, and Thomas Elias Gillham 30, all of Hennock. Mr Harold C Thornbery, a director of Ferrubron Manufacturing Co Ltd of Bermondsey, said that in 1930 11 or 12 men were employed underground at the mine and six were now dead, though not all had died of silicosis.[10]*

Silicosis is caused by the inhalation of very fine silica dust that can be generated by drilling and blasting rock, such as granite, that contains a high proportion of silica. It is controlled by using water flush drills, good ventilation and the systematic wetting of any broken rock before it is moved. One wonders how the jury arrived at the conclusion that *every known precaution was taken by the employers* as this certainly was not the case when the author worked there some 30 years later, in 1963.

On Slatter's death 'Old Man' Tucker assumed the functions of a Mine Manager under the close supervision of one of the directors, S J Hann, who was based in London. Perhaps the local term of Mine Captain might better have described his position.[11]

This is an appropriate point to summarise the layout of the mine and its orebodies. At Great Rock there is a series of mineralised structures running approximately East-West that were ultimately mined from both sides of the

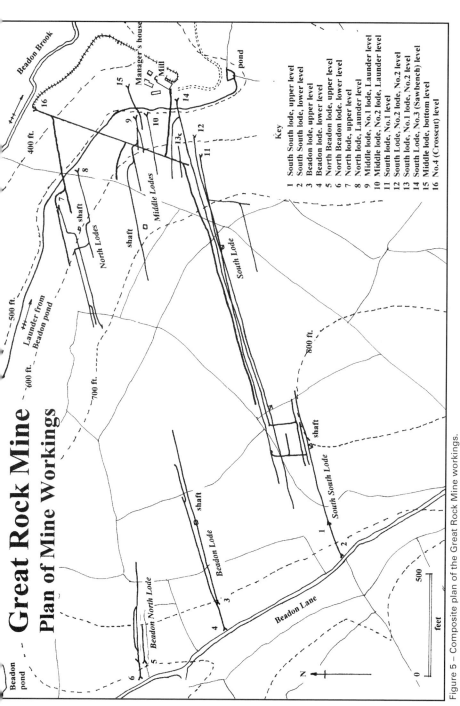

Figure 5 – Composite plan of the Great Rock Mine workings.

hill. **Figure 5** is a composite plan of the mine workings. On the east or mill side there were three sets of structures namely: North lodes, Middle lodes and South lode. The North and Middle lodes were not single lodes but a number of parallel structures carrying erratic and unpredictable mineralisation. Only South Lode (sometimes referred to as Main South Lode) had a main leader and was continuous.

Work also started on driving two levels east on a lode discovered on the west side of the hill close to Beadon Lane **Figure 6**. The dates on the section show when the tunnels reached these points. Again there was more than one structure here, which could be the westward extension of the Middle Lodes.

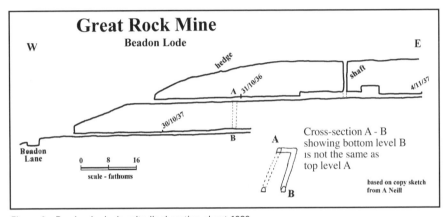

Figure 6 – Beadon Lode, longitudinal section about 1939.

Ore from the lower of the two levels could be trammed straight out and dumped into a bin above the road for subsequent cartage to the mill. The original copy sketch from which **Figure 6** derived was titled *Old Lode Beadon Lane to Shaft in Walling's Field*. On the top right hand side of the sketch was a note:

Anticipated ore been worked out surface to dotted line to hedge. Not known whether ore has been taken beyond or west of the shaft.

Unfortunately the dotted line does not appear on the sketch. However, I infer that this means the ground east of the shaft and probably refers to old shallow surface workings, date unknown.

For years the mainstay of the mine had been the South Lode. By the 1930's this was almost worked out down to Sawbench (No.3) Level and the mine had to be deepened to maintain production. The levels worked up to this time were driven straight into the hillside following the lodes from their outcrop. Because of the topography it was not possible to drive another level directly below No.3. Some ore was being produced from a winze or pit sunk to follow a pay zone below No.3 Level. The only way that the mine could be deepened was either by sinking a shaft from a location somewhere close to the mill or by driving a deep crosscut adit in from the bottom of the Beadon valley below the mine. The crosscut was decided upon. This crosscut was to be driven in south from just above stream level and was to be placed just inside the granite contact shown as No.16 on **Figure 5**. This position gave the deepest possible level with the minimum of tunnelling. One advantage of the crosscut was that it would intersect all of the lodes already exploited higher in the mine, and might possibly discover new lodes not found in the upper levels.

Plate 15 – Incline down to Crosscut Level (© Tucker collection)

No.4 Level, or Crosscut Level, was a major capital project and was driven in dead straight for 700 ft.. To access this development an incline was constructed from close to the mill down to the valley floor by the Beadon Brook. Wagons were hauled up the incline using a second-hand steam winch that worked on compressed air[12] **Plate 15**. This relatively poor photograph is the only one that I have found of this incline. Part-way down is a wagon while at the bottom two further wagons can just be made out.

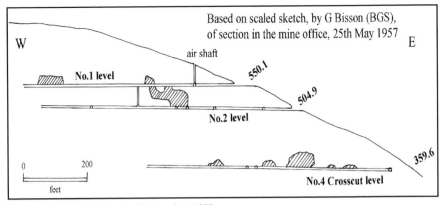

Figure 7 – North Lode longitudinal section, 1957.

From the bottom of the incline rail tracks ran round the contour and into Crosscut Level entrance. The tunnels on this level were driven considerably wider than the old upper levels and the opportunity was taken to increase the gauge of the track to 24 inches which permitted the use of larger wagons. Additional hands were taken on at this time. Two of them, Bill Chubb and Arnold Chubb, father and son from Cornwall, worked on the Crosscut Level.[13]

As Crosscut Level was driven south it first intersected North Lode **Figure 7** and then Middle Lode. Both these lodes were subsequently driven on and some stoping was done, however results were disappointing.

The main target was South Lode and this was finally intersected at the end of the crosscut. South Lode on No.4 Level was to become the mainstay of the mine for the next few years. Once a connection had been made with the winze below No.3 Level, the air pipe was routed in through No.3 and down to No.4[14]

H G Dines, of the British Geological Survey, visited the mine in 1938. His report[15] briefly notes operations and the washing plant, **Figure 8**.

> *Two waterwheels and a turbine, also a Petter oil engine. Compressed air hoists used underground. Work used to be confined to the main lode and in 1933 there were no reserves. The property was then prospected and other lodes found. A crosscut is now being driven in the bottom of the valley to assist exploitation of the lower levels.*

A sketch longitudinal section shows two levels, a 40 ft. level and a 80 ft. level, extending east and west from a winze sunk below No.3 South lode.

Reserves now stand at about 2 years supply. The lodes are in the killas as well as the granite but are thin there. In the granite they vary up to 3 or 4 feet, but are usually a foot or less. Both walls are much altered for 2 or 3 feet on either side and contain strings of ore.

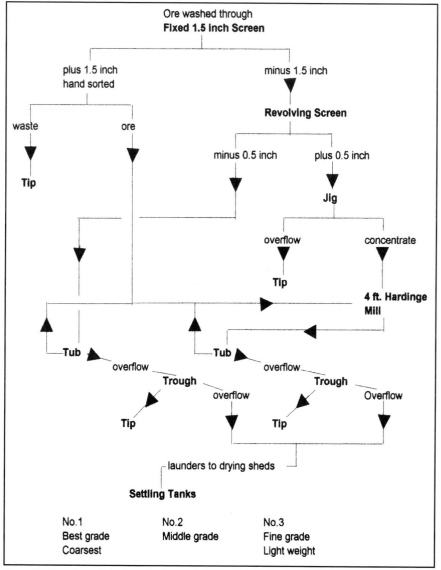

Figure 8 – Flowsheet of the Great Rock washing plant in 1938 is based on a sketch in Dine's notes.

Plate 16 The washing plant in about 1936, (© Tucker collection) The mine bungalow is on the right. At the top is the compressor house and to the left is the tramway to the ore bin and wash box. Production was about 300 tons per year.

1. Pers comm. Stafford Clark. 1 June 1999.
2. Letter from KWC Middleton, Branch Manager, Commercial Union Assurance Co Ltd., to the Deputy General Manager, London, 17 May 1926.
3. KMPS Newsletter, June 1995.
4. Mining Journal, 26 November 1927.
5. Mining Journal, 7 January 1928, report for 1927
6. Hine W., Hennock & Teign Village, 1977.
7. Inteview – Tom Howard & Bill May, 26 January 1984, C le Marchant.
8. Interview – Archie Cudmore, 20th January 1984, C le Marchant.
9. Letter from Ron Tucker, KMPS Newsletter, February 1995. Ron Tucker, Young Charlie's son, later worked at the New Consols mine 1947-52 and later at Hingston Downs Quarry.
10. Cornish Post and Mining News, 12th December 1935.
11. Letter from Norman Bennett to the author, 4 January 1983.
12. Ron Tucker – interview 8th April 2002, author.
13 Ron Tucker – interview 8th April 2002, author.
14. Interview – Alfred Hodge, 29th January 1984, C le Marchant.
15. Report dated 9th June 1938 – BGS files Exeter.

CHAPTER FIVE

WORLD WAR TWO

During the 1939-1945 war, when men were called up, several women came to work at the lighter jobs, the first employed starting in 1943. Later in the war the mining here became a 'reserved' occupation.[1]

Frank Michell, **Plate 17**, a lecturer from the world famous Camborne School of Metalliferous Mining, was employed as a consultant from about 1940 when the company decided that they should have a mine plan. Michell came from a well known Redruth family which had been involved in Cornish mining for several generations. He had graduated from the School of Mines in 1931, and shortly afterwards joined the staff as lecturer in mineral dressing. He later went on to become Head of Mineral Dressing and Vice Principal of the School.

'Porky' Michell, as we irreverently used to refer to him when we were students, was rather a shy man and was not the most dynamic of lecturers. That said he certainly knew mineral dressing and many of his students went on to successful careers in this field.

Michell's mine plan was completed in October 1940. It is a particularly valuable document. The original plan was coloured but has subsequently been updated, the updates are not coloured so we can see exactly the position of the underground workings at the end of 1940[a]. I have been unable to find the longitudinal sections that were produced at the same time.

Michell was responsible for the only published technical paper that describes the workings of the mine and the washing plant. It was written in 1944 but the methods, particularly in the washing plant, had not changed since the 1930's. He wrote:

Plate 17 – Frank Bice Michell
about 1960 (Author collection)

[a] In 1983 this original mine plan was held by the Geological Dept. at Leicester University who at that time used the North Lode workings for practical work. Enquiries to the Department in 2002 failed to locate the plan.

At Great Rock the lodes have been much more extensively worked than elsewhere over a number of years and, although patchy, considerable areas have been stoped. There are three main lodes, all striking approximately east to west and dipping north from 60 to 85 degrees, but the bulk of the workings are on the South lode, where it has been opened up by adits on four horizons. **Figure 9.** *The lode varies in dip from almost vertical to about 70 degrees, whilst the strike is regular except where it has been cut by small cross veins and joints. The lode has been stoped on and off for a total length of some 1,750 ft. along strike and from the outcrop down to the present bottom level, 430 ft. below the highest point at the surface.*

Two other lodes have been worked, namely the Middle and the North lodes, but bunches of haematite are more sporadic here. In addition, there are a number of stringers, usually of insufficient width and purity to be stoped, although a small amount of work has been done on some of these.

As a general rule, it may be said that the values die out on approaching the granite margin and, although fissures persist in the adjoining culm measures, they pinch to a few inches and consist of quartz, the haematite being almost absent.

Originally the lodes were discovered by pitting on the hill-side, after which adits were driven on the course of the lode, all the ore being trammed to a washing plant via these adits. As the working proceeded, the lodes were followed by winzing and, later, a cross-cut adit was driven

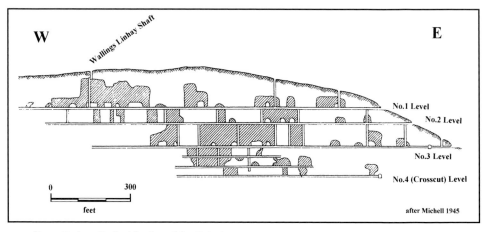

Figure 9 – Longitudinal Section of South Lode

from the lowest point in the valley to intersect all of the lodes, well inside the granite contact. At the present time it is from this level that all the ore is being won and is hoisted by way of an incline to the washing plant.

In all, from the highest point of the outcrop to this bottom adit, over 400 ft. of lode has been worked. On the eastern side of the same hill, some 2,300 ft. along the strike, lodes at Beadon lane have been developed in more recent years. These lodes, only 20 ft. apart, appear to be a continuation of the North lodes, and have yielded good quality ore.

In general, the lodes on the property are fairly narrow, although bunches of up to 5 ft. and 6 ft. wide have been known, and are stoped by resuing.[b] The stripped country rock being used as stope filling. All stoping is overhand and carried up from stulls.

As work proceeds, bratticing is carried up at either end of the stope for access, whilst similar brattices are constructed so as to form ore passes for the removal of broken ore. The lode is easily broken and is mucked into these passes whilst the wall rock is stripped to obtain a stoping width and used as filling. **Figure 10**

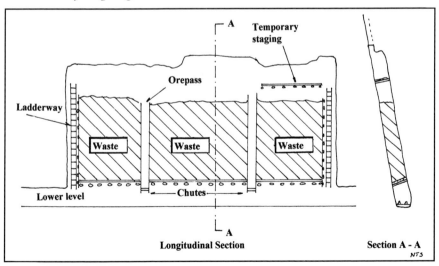

Figure 10 – Schematic stope layout.

[b] Resuing is a method sometimes used for mining very narrow orebodies, perhaps less than a foot wide. In a steeply dipping orebody such as Great Rock, the ore is blasted out some 2-4 feet ahead of the stope face and sent to the mill. The stope is then widened to 2 to 3 feet, sufficiently wide for a man to work in, by blasting out the waste alongside the slot previously created when blasting the ore. The broken waste rock falls to the bottom of the stope and is left as fill.

In the washing plant the ore passes through a simple but effective treatment and the flowsheet is probably unique **Figure 11**. *From the ore bins the ore is withdrawn over a washing screen having 7/8-in holes, where much of the micaceous haematite disintegrates. Large pieces of barren rock are removed by hand,* (and sent to tip) *whilst any fragments carrying mineral values are also broken* (to a size suitable for the Hardinge mill).

The undersize from this screen is then sized in a revolving trommel making three products, plus 5/8 in., minus 5/8 in. plus 20-mesh, and minus 20-mesh. Undersize from the 20-mesh screen carries the bulk of the haematite and is washed in a tank or boil-box, from which the coarse

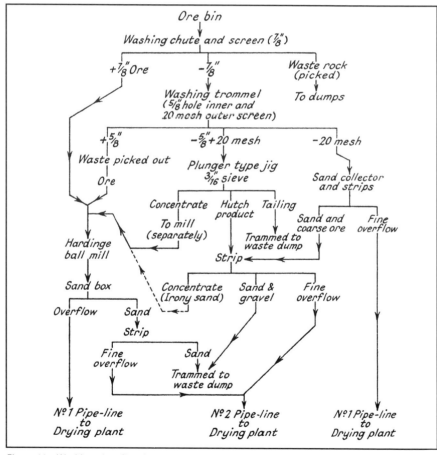

Figure 11 – Washing plant flowsheet 1945.

sand is removed and discarded whilst the overflow passes to strips or sluices **Plate 19**.

Overflow from the tailraces of these sluices constitutes the finished product and the accumulated sand is rewashed to make a No.2 grade. Coarse sand is rejected, whilst any ferruginous sands are ground and washed. The plus 20-mesh passes to a jig of the fixed sieve type having an accelerated pulsion stroke and jigging is carried out using a 3/16-in. grating. All jig tailing is rejected, the concentrate being ground and re-washed, whilst the hutch product is either reground or rewashed in

Plate 18 – Interior of the mill, August 1945. The revolving trommel or screen is top right. The diagonal chute brought the lump ore down to the floor for loading into the Hardinge mill that is off pic-ture to the right, The fine sand and mineral runs down the chute to the left and thence into the sluice. The woman on the left with the shovel is Phyllis Warren. © British Geological Survey.

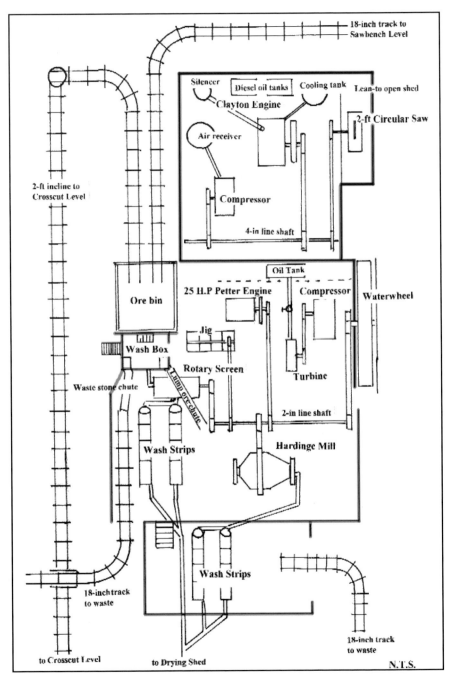

Figure 12 Washing plant schematic layout – based on a sketch by Arthur Ball. 1949.

strips, depending upon the amount of pyrite present. All plus 7/8-in. material is ground in a small Hardinge mill which is run in open circuit with a high water solids ratio and a light ball load. The mill discharges into a sand box, the overflow being washed in sluices making a finished product and sand. The iron rich head of the strips and the hutch material is ground in separate batches and washed for a No.2 quality haematite.

The use of such a low percentage of solids together with a light load in the mill is due to the fact that over-grinding of silicious material must be avoided and the object is more to disintegrate the aggregate of tiny plates of haematite than to break them.

The settling pits are arranged in series, the best material being obtained from the first pit, because colloidal silicious slime, such as clay, slightly contaminates the overflow, which passes into subsequent pits and goes to market as a No.2 grade.

After the accumulated haematite has settled it is pierced with poles to assist the exudation of water and colloidal material which is drained off.[2]

Plate 19 – The setting pits at the drying sheds about 1929 (© Tucker collection)

Sam Bradford recalled:

They used to have three lots of tanks there. The best work used to drop into the first and the overflow from that used to go into the second and then the third.....this was the best stuff, you see, the first tanks. And then when a tank was full up – before the tank was full up – we had a long spear, it had a long blade with a handle on, and we used to have a board across and shift 'im up as we's want to do, and they pushed this 'ere spear right down into the ore and that used to let air and stuff up through and make the ore settle solid[a]....clean it out with your shovel and drive it in for drying.[3] **Plate 20.**

George Stancombe is seen here in the foreground holding, what appears to be, such a pole tipped with a metal spike. Note the barrels stacked in the bushes.

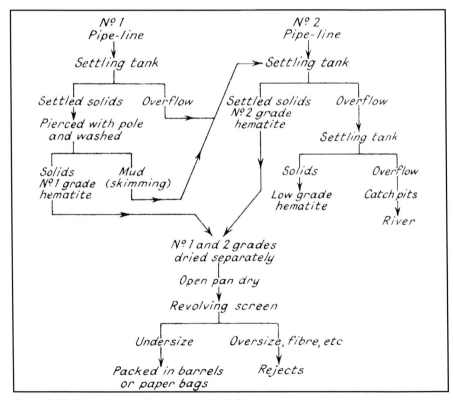

Figure 13. Drying and Packing Plant flowsheet – 1945

[a] The 'spear' was used to break up flocculated (aggregated) particles of haematite to allow entrapped water to rise

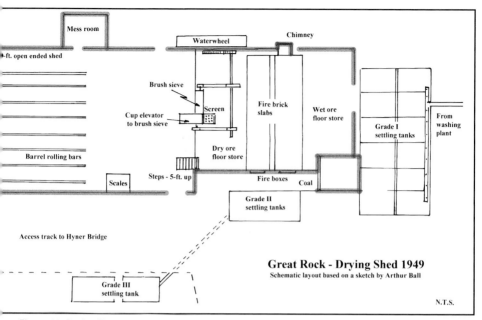

Figure 14 Drying Plant schematic layout – 1949

The thickened haematite was then dried on an open hearth (with a firebrick tiled floor over brick flues) similar to those used in the china clay industry, screened to remove fragments of foreign material with a fine-mesh screen and finally packed in casks for transit. **Figures 13** and **14.**

Ron Tucker remembers the drying shed[4]

The drying-shed furnace was operated continuously, seven days a week, and burned good quality coal to ensure that the fire stayed-in overnight. The first job of the day was to rake the ashes and build up the fire. There was no shelter provided for the fire-door or the coal.....

Sid Preston described working there:[5]

Used clogs down the drying sheds 'cos they had to go in on top the ovens what they used to spread the ore on for to dry....had to take that off every morning. Put it on in the morning through the day, banked up at night and then when you take it off you had shovel it off you had to shovel off all red hot.....boots ain't no good, all your nails would fall out.....used to have clogs then.... didn't last long if you didn't any irons on 'em.

Ron Tucker again:

From Great Rock, regular shipments of ore were made to Germany. During the early years at the drying sheds of Great Rock Mine ore was packed for delivery to customers in wooden casks of varying sizes from 5 cwts to as much as 10 cwts. Barrels for Great Rock and Kelly were purchased second-hand from Cullompton; a lorry journey being made from Great Rock each month for this purpose, with the lorry returning piled high with empty barrels.[6]

These casks were pre-used and had contained fruit juices, frying fat etc. The end of the barrel was removed by slackening the steel hoops. The ore entered via a funnel and cloth apron cover from the elevator and sieve and rocked on a 1 inch square steel bar to compact fullness. **Figure 15**

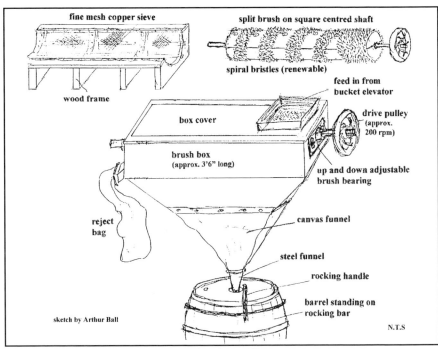

Figure 15 – Revolving sieving gear at the drying plant, 1948

Sam Bradford would weigh the empty cask before and after filling, and after replacing the end would drift back and secure the hoops, paint the ends white and stencil the Gross, Tare and Nett weights in black. Sam was an expert cooper and could repair casks with spare staves from one to another. To complete an order of say 16 tons, the weights of each barrel would have to be totalled, numbered and marked. An improvement to this method of filling was carried out by drilling a 2.5 inch hole in the cask head with an electric pillar hole saw for the funnel entry, and using the wooden hole plug wrapped in cloth as a bung, securing it in place by nailing it over with tinplate.[7]

Sam Bradford[8]

When the barrels were full....I used to go and cooper up these casks....drift up the hoops....and then they had to be marked where they had to go. Used to have stencils, mark 'em with white paint and used to put FMC, Ferrubron Manufacturing Co., FMC on the top and then the weight, and where they had to go....We used to send it all over the place, Australia, Canada, New Zealand and France used to have a lot and we even send some over to, one time I marked up, Yugoslavia....the stencils were put on H O Belgrade....There used to be a big brickworks down at Heathfield.....they used to take some....stain they used to call it....used to have the third grade.

The firm at Wolverhampton called Griffiths used to take a lot. There was chemists attached to this firm....they used to bring down plates of this paint, different plates and we put them on a long rack....see how long it kept with the weather....they used to test it....down at the drying sheds.

Clifford Wills who also worked there in 1938-39 recalls:[9]

At one time, they used forty gallon steel drums to pack the ore in and a drum of ore would weigh between 10 and 11 cwt, depending on quality..... the tops of the barrels were taken out and the barrels filled with ore. The ore ran in through a brass funnel which fitted into the round hole in the middle cover over the barrel. The barrels stood on a big granite slab – the slab came from Dartmoor somewhere, Merrivale[c] possibly. It was about one inch thick and five foot to six foot square. They tried to use a steel plate but the barrels used to slide around all over the place. There used to be five or six blokes just washing the ore.

Great Rock used to send away four grades of ore. The third grade from Great Rock used to be sent over to Germany where it was added to

[c] Merrivale is a granite quarry close to the B3357 on the western edge of Dartmoor

graphite grease, I think. The first grade went all over the country to make paint. Down in Bovey Tracey the barber used to use it to put on his razor strops to put a fine edge on his cut-throat razors. The water running off the settling tanks at Great Rock was practically clean.

In 1942 Old Man Tucker retired. After Edmund Slatter went to Exeter, Old Man Tucker and his family had moved down from the village to live in the mine office bungalow. He now moved just up the lane into the lower of the two staff bungalows. His son, Young Charlie Tucker, moved into the mine office bungalow and also took over the job of Mine Manager.

During the war some of the men left to join the armed services. In July 1943 the labour force on the mine was 17[10] made up as follows

	Number	Total Wages	Hours/week
Men (21 years and over)	13	£55.11.9	528
Youths and boys (under 21)	1	£2.8.7	44
Women (18 years and over)	2	£8.12.9	72
Girls (under 18 years)	1	£2.15.0	44

Norman Bennett recalls[11] that

During the war years when there was little demand for the pigment because of the scarcity of paint medium.

In the closing months of the 1939-45, S J Hann was Chairman with H Todd Thornbery, son of Russell Thornbery co-director and Mrs Devenish (then Miss Truman and my secretary) as Secretary of the Company. All, myself included, were associated with Griffiths Bros & Co. London Ltd. which held 49% of Ferrubron Manufacturing Company shares. There was also a director named Gibbons who represented a South African land company which was a shareholder.

H G Dines and J A Robbie, from the Geological Survey, visited the mine in October 1942. Dines's notes[12] are reproduced below:

Main South Lode is the chief producer and has been very extensively stoped down to 4th or adit level which is 72 fathoms deep under the hill. Lode dips north between 45 degrees and vertical. It is 2.5 feet wide solid haematite in places and at western end of workings is down to 1 foot.

Middle Lode is much flatter than the others dipping about 40 degrees north. In west end of workings peters out into strings.

North lodes, there are two, are much steeper but dip north. One crosses the mouth of the main adit, the other is 20 or 30 yds. in. Yielded some good ore but peters out to strings in western end. Some crystals of pyrite up to an eighth of an inch across occur in the haematite here. Elsewhere there appears to be no impurities beyond country rock which is chloritized granite adjacent to the walls.

Very little water issues from the main adit which connects all workings on North, Middle and Main South lodes. The Beadon workings are very wet and can only be worked in summer. The Beadon lode was not cut in the crosscut but a dozen very narrow lodes were cut in it.

A little later the Beadon North Lode was photographed **Plate 20**. This was taken looking up at the lode in the roof of the tunnel. Some ore has been re-moved as evidenced by the timber stulls across the ex-cavation. The timbers are about 3 ft. long.

Output was then some 300 tons per year, treating about 1200 tons of ore.

Plate 20 – Beadon North Lode, August 1945 (© British Geological Survey)

In the List of Mines for 1945, it was reported that at Great Rock there were 10 men working on surface and 6 men underground. Ferrubron Manufacturing Co. Ltd.'s address was given as 29 Mack's Road, London. This information should be treated with some caution as E M Slatter was still shown as the Agent (manager), and **Plate 21** shows 4 women workers in front of the washing plant.

Plate 21 Washing plant and mine office, August 1945. (© British Geological Survey)

1. Hine W., Hennock & Teign Village, 1977.
2. Michell F. B., Mineral Pigments, Mine & Quarry Engineering, January 1945, P9-14.
3. Interview – Sam Bradford, 26 July 1973, B Brett.
4. KMPS September 1996 – Extracts of notes recorded from Mr Ron Tucker.
5. Interview – Sid Preston, 17th January 1984. C le Marchant.
6. KMPS Sept 1996 – Extracts of notes recorded from Mr Ron Tucker.
7. KMPS Newsletter, June 1998.
8. Interview – Sam Bradford, 26 July 1993. B.Brett. KMPS.
9. KMPS Newsletter November 1998 – interview with Clifford Wills reminiscences 1938-9.
10. Return to Ministry of Labour and National Service – July 1943
11. Norman Bennett letter to author, 4th January 1983.
12. Hand written notes on visit, 15th October 1942, in BGS archives at Exeter.

Young Charlie Tucker resigned in about 1948 to take up a post with the New Consols Mine at Luckett in Cornwall which was then being opened up. He later went on to work in the mill at the little Hawkswood wolfram mine on the fringe of Bodmin Moor.[a] **Plate 22**, Charlie Tucker is fourth from the left.

Plate 22 - Staff at Hawkswood Mine, 1953 (Finch collection)

[a] For further information on Hawkswood and Cornwall's Wolfram mines see the author's book 'Castle-an-Dinas' 1916-1967 – Cornish Hillside Publications 2001.

He had taken the job of manager at Great Rock and had kept the mine running, however he had been appointed more on the basis of being the son of his father rather than on his own mining and management abilities.[1]

The new manager was Sydney Taylor, who was originally from Yorkshire. On leaving school he went into coal mining, working his way up from pit pony driver to under-manager. He served in the RAF during the war returning from the Far-East in 1945 with the rank of Squadron Leader. **Plate 23**. He was seconded to the Coal Control Commission in Germany until 1948 when he took over as Mine Manager at Great Rock.[2]

The Taylors lived in the bungalow for a short while, then they moved to Lustleigh

The methods used in the mine and in the mill in 1949 had hardly changed since the death of Slatter in 1933. There was no electricity apart from a dynamo which provided some lighting.[3] This dynamo was put in by Ron Tucker when he was demobbed after the war. The labour intensive washing plant and drying shed were all powered by water.

The arrival of Sydney Taylor as manager brought new ideas and over the years he successfully modernised many aspect of the mine. His attempts at modernisation did not please everybody, and one or two of the older employees felt that things would have been better left as they were. But times had moved on and, with rapidly increasing labour costs, the old labour intensive methods, particularly in the mill, were no longer economic.

Plate 23 - Sydney Taylor in RAF uniform, 1945
(© Taylor collection)

At much the same time Arthur Ball joined the mine as the mine's fitter or engineer. It was through Arthur Ball's improvisation and practical engineering skill that many of the ideas and designs put together by Sydney Taylor and Frank Michell were turned into reality. There was little money for new machinery and use had to be made of second-hand and scrap materials wherever possible.

In the mill the washing strips were replaced by spiral classifiers and shaking tables. Two of the shaking tables came from Bridford Barytes mine - the third was bought new from Holman Bros. of Camborne in Cornwall. Everything else was made on the mine, even the spiral classifiers that replaced the strips as Arthur Ball described:

Spiral blades - used to cut out the discs, and weld 'em together, tie it to a tree and use the lorry - pull 'em out to any length you wanted - perfect! [4]

The wooden launders from the washing sheds down to the drying sheds were replaced by twin pipe lines. The washing plant now produced 2 products - high quality GRI and lower quality GRX. At the drying sheds, **Figures 16 & 17**, cyclones and a drum filter were installed to handle the GRI material and Braithwaite tanks to settle the GRX product.

These systems largely replaced the labour intensive settling pits. The old coal/wood fired drying beds were replaced by two oil fired rotary dryers. The first rotary drier was purchased and a second bigger one, with 3 burners instead of 2, was made in the mine's workshop. **Figure 18**. Other improvements included extending the loading bay.

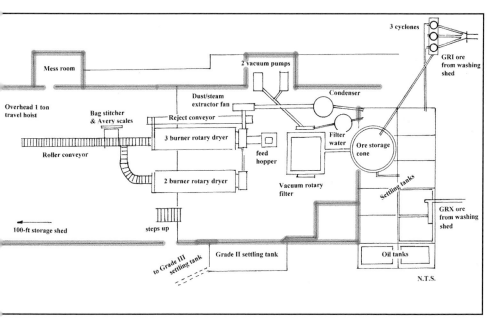

Figure 16 - Drying plant flowsheet in its final form - 1969. Schematic layout based on a sketch by Arthur Ball.

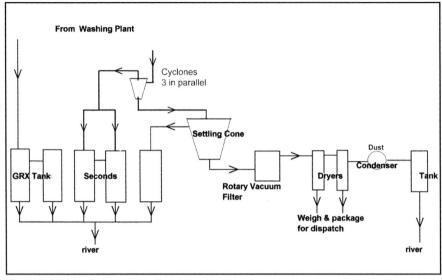

Figure 17 - Schematic layout of drying plant - 1969

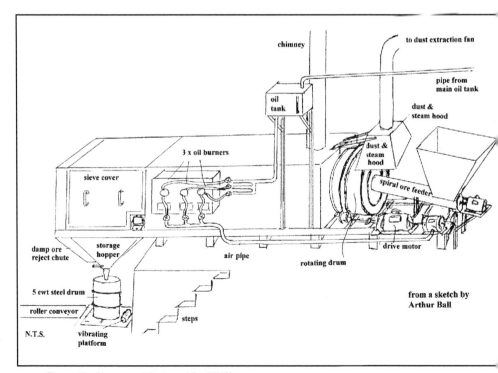

Figure 18 - 'Home made' rotary drier (1969)

Plate 24 - Drying sheds, 1961
© J Hamilton, Author collection)

Plate 24 taken in 1961, is the only photograph that I have managed to find of the drying sheds. The redundant waterwheel is in the foreground with the roof of the drying shed behind. To the right is the covered loading bay.

Up in the plant area new workshops were built **Plate 25**. This included left to right: sawmill, workshop, store and garage. The winch for the incline is in front of the buildings.

Underground the ore reserves position had become precarious and development failed to expose fresh orebodies. At the end of the war Frank Michell was asked to report on the mine and he submitted a discouraging view of the 'ore reserves' which he thought would last only perhaps another five years at the most.

Plate 25 - New workshop buildings, about 1950 (© Manley collection)

67

Frank Michell, in a letter[5] to the author recorded that:

Over the years we did quite a lot of prospecting by searching for float stones[b] and following up by trenching and pitting but never any size lodes were found. We also kept an eye on the trench dug for a new water pipe for Torquay and carried out a variometric survey between Beadon and the Hennock side of the hill. Unfortunately the haematite was less magnetic than the wall rock and we found the anomalies indicated stoped out (and often filled) lode![6]

This geophysical work was carried out by members of the Department of Geology, University of Nottingham during the summer of 1951[7] using both electric and magnetic geophysical methods. No new orebodies were discovered. Interestingly one of the men involved in this work was a Mr Devenish. Possibly he was a relative of Mrs Devenish, who was then Norman Bennett's secretary. She later became a director of Ferrubron.

Frank Michell went on:

The lodes at Great Rock seem to consist of two sets of fissures with a small difference in strike and when they intersect mineralisation increases and a workable lode results. Sometimes at these intersections, mineralised fissures run away on one of these joints. Formerly driving was carried out along the vein as a means of exploring such branches. This proved laboursome and I introduced drilling into (or at right angles) to the main vein in order to explore any branch vein. This was fairly simple using jointed steels and sampling the sludge which of course showed the 'tell tale' colour when a vein was intersected.

Stan Godfrey, one of the miners used to do the deep drilling:

We used to deep drill....from a level they would put in a hole say 50 ft....if we picked up mineral in that....we drove a crosscut to that and that how we prove that. Bill Wills....me and him used to do the majority of the deep drilling....we worked on this evening, we had only gone in a matter of a foot and the drill just shot away.. (into the soft lode)

"Must be at least 2 ft of mineral here" - *and that was only a foot away from the level.*[8]

---

[b] Float stones are pieces of rock which are found on the surface above the soil and which can be indicative of the underlying geology.

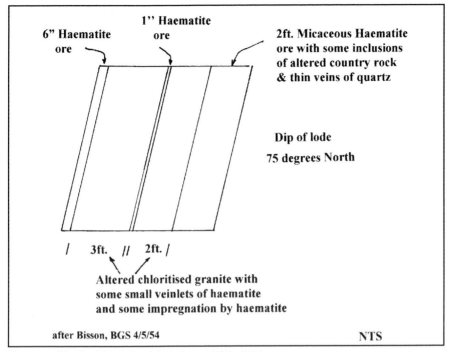

Figure 19 - Sketch of South South Lode face at 750ft - 1954

G.Bisson, from the British Geological Survey, reported in May 1954,[9] that a new lode known as South South Lode, was being investigated by an adit on the Beadon side. From the portal to 580 ft. the adit followed barren or almost barren closed fissures in granite. Two pay shoots were found: the first, from 580 ft. to 710 ft. was from 4 ins. to 3 ft. 6 ins. wide, averaging 2 ft. wide; the second from 730 ft. to 750 ft. was also 2 ft. wide. The face at 750 ft. was mapped and recorded **Figure 19**.

As a result of this discovery, it was intended to crosscut to the lode from the Main South Lode at a horizon about 100 ft. below the level of the Beadon South South Lode adit. This would, when connected, provide ventilation and make possible through haulage to the mill on the east side of the hill.

A further lode was being investigated near the crest of the hill, the lode having been located from hearsay of 18 ins. of haematite cut during laying of a water main from Tottiford reservoir over the hill. A shaft was sunk on it for 60 ft. and a drive west had followed it for 50 ft..

The shaft, Plantation Shaft, lay on the hill top above the mill and was sunk on lode. The shaft timbering supported a ladderway down one side of the shaft and a skipway on the other side. The skip ran through double doors fitted over the top of the hoisting compartment upon which were fitted rails to permit a tram to be run under the bottom dumping skip once it had been hoisted up in the headframe. The skip was hoisted by a compressed air winch housed in a small corrugated iron building close to the shaft, the hoisting rope passing over a sheave wheel mounted upon a neat wooden headgear. The tramway ran off to a nearby shaft down which the ore was

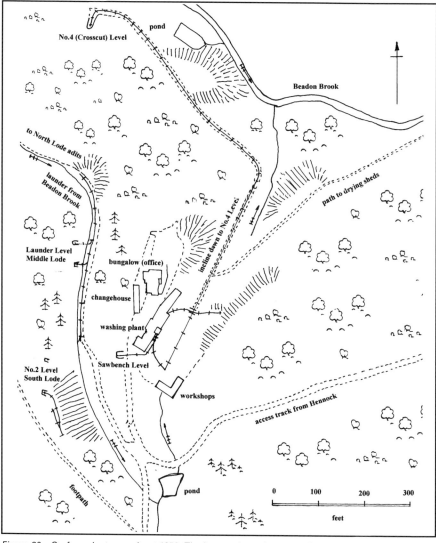

Figure 20 – Surface plant area about 1953. The layout shown here remained unaltered until the mine closed in 1969.

tipped through old workings to a tramming level far below. The compressed-air pipeline for the winch, pump and rock drills emerged through the same shaft. A set of points in the tramway allowed a tram to be sent off to a waste dump along the hillside.[10]

Bisson returned in May 1957, by which time considerable work had been done on the South South Lode:[11]

In the No.1 crosscut, south from No.2 level on the Main South Lode at about 290 ft. from the portal, thin lodes were encountered at 150 ft. and at 160 ft. This more southerly lode, never more than 1 or 3 ins. wide, was followed for about 60 ft. where it petered out, and the northern one picked up and followed for a further 240 ft., with limited stoping above the level of ore up to 9 ins..

The No.2 crosscut driven south from No.2 level on Main South Lode at 1450 ft. from the portal, with the intention of intersecting the South South Lode, at about 100 ft. below the level of the adit which was originally driven on this lode from the west side of the hill. As no lode has been found which is definitely the South South Lode, it is planned to sink on the latter from the adit to trace its course downwards.

In the No.2 crosscut lodes were encountered at about 35 ft., followed 60 ft. to the west and known as No.1 level west; at about 65 ft., followed 160 ft. to the east and called No.1 level east; and at about 155 ft., followed 50 ft. to the east and called No.2 level east. In stopes above No.1 level east ore up to 18 ins. wide has been mined. In No.2 level east only traces of ore have been found along a well-defined joint.

Underground, carbide[c] hand-lamps were preferred to the smaller cap-lamps. The cap-lamps were relatively heavy and difficult to attach to the resin impregnated felt hats worn by the miners up to the end of the 1950's. The hand lamps were supplied to the Ferrubron Mining Company by the Premier Lamp and Engineering Co. Ltd.. According to sales records held by Premier, 58 hand lamps were supplied to the mine between 1955 and 1960.

Using carbide lights underground required a daily routine. Before the shift started the miners made their way to the purpose built carbide store at the rear of the mine workshop and fitters' shop. Here they filled their personal carbide tin, usually small cocoa or syrup tins, from one of the steel drums containing lump carbide. During this period carbide was easily

---

[c] Strictly speaking these were acetylene lamps, the acetylene gas being generated by carefully adding water to calcium carbide. Miners always referred to them as carbide lamps or lights.

available from many sources including Halfords, agricultural merchants and even camping shops (though not in such large drums).

A licence was required to store more than 28 lbs. of calcium carbide and certain conditions were required before a certificate was issued. The carbide had to be stored in a separate room which had to be dry. Drums had to be stored on a raised platform and had to be opened with a special tool - not a hammer and chisel. No smoking or naked lights were allowed in the store room.

The miners then made their way to the level where they had finished work the previous day. At the end of that shift hand-lamps would have been left outside the level, the water regulator being turned off and the lamps left to burn off the remaining acetylene gas. For the new morning shift the carbide chamber was removed from the lamp, the contents sieved to retain any good unused calcium carbide to which new was added to the chamber. The lamp was re-assembled, the water regulator turned on and the gas jet ignited using matches. Miners at Great Rock seldom used reflectors on their hand-lamps, they preferred to use them without, although producing a less bright light there was less to clean. Spent carbide was never disposed of underground it was always removed to the surface and discarded onto a small heap outside the carbide store.[12]

Gerald Adcock who worked on the mine from the 1950's up until closure gives us a view of the miner's job: (See Figure 10, page 51)

Timbering

> *You used to get paid for each piece of timber. All the timber had to be cut....we used to take out little notches in the wall, little squares and each timber had its own. We used to make what we call measuring sticks. We used to go up in the woods and cut out a hazel tree and take the measurement of the pole and how much gap was from the top to the bottom so they drove in tight. You see they were only let in the wall. We used to have a chisel, like an old cold chisel, which was broken drill steel we used to sharpen that and we used to make notches in the wall. Had to trim the timber on the ends it was like a square. We drove it to a square shape and the other end of the timber to the angle of the wall and then drove it down until it got tight......The footwall would be the one you took your notch out, the hanging wall you would be driving down on.*

Stoping

What you used to do, you would go up. You would work off what we called a platform and we would have to do the same as what we done there - notched the timber, put the poles up and then work off them. Drill it, take the poles and the staging down every night before you blast.....You had to take it down or else when you came in next morning it would be all broke with the blasting, you see. And when you got up, well enough room so you could work above where you were going to put your stoping floor in, then you could start putting your floor in and you laid granite over that. As you went up you closed your chute for the ore to come out of the stope and you'd build a box in the bottom with a couple of boards so you could put in a bar and lever it away and let it out.

The ore had to be hand sorted - all the granite would be sorted out after the blast. As you were digging it over with a pick you would pick out all the granite and just keep the ore dust. That would help you build your stope up. But once you got up a certain height, 'cos you took out so much you would have to start staging, what we call staging, and you would go up through then. May come that you have to put in another false floor. You also keep, what you call, your stope chute upright so the ore doesn't hang as you throw it down the chutes 'cos you can go right through to the surface like which we did. We went through into a couple of fields, I can remember one with Stan Godfrey, we went right into a potato field - we had potatoes and mangles down in the stope....that was the one at Beadon.

Used to stand in the middle and you has to drill it so it broke away from the middle first in a Vee shape....the first 3 charges to go off at the same time so it blew it all out in one piece and the circling holes could go off afterwards.... Your first job in the morning would be to get on your staging with an iron bar to clear all the loose granite. Mind you had some lumps big as that (referring to a window) *used to slide down out of the walls. Sometimes it hit the staging - down you would go with it. When it landed on the pile you would put, what we call a plaster on it, a stick of dynamite with clay on it to break it just so we could handle it.*

When I first went out they had the carbide - the old carbide lights. Sometimes you go to light up....you would stand beside him (the miner) *while he lit, and he be lighting up and the fuses, when they go off, they throw out a certain gas. Sometimes they blew out the light. So there would be a panic....of course the carbide light would be blocked or something - you would start panicking.... So he would take your light, one light between you to get down through the stope an that. Sometimes you would just about get down to the bottom when the first would go off - the wind from it would knock 'ee against the wall. We used stand and count them* (the shots) *so we would know in the morning if there were any miss-fires. We had a lot because it was very very damp in there - used to take our dynamite underground with us when we went in breakfast time. Used to come out and say how many holes you were drilling, how much dynamite you want and how many detonators you want - and they have to stay in there until you are ready in the evening to blast. Used to blast about 3 o'clock in the afternoon.... Breakfast was, I think, half-past nine ten o'clock, something like that.*

Before electricity was installed at the Great Rock drying sheds, three carbide hand-lamps were used for illumination during winter overtime when dried ore was packed into barrels. Just imagine the scene as the lonely worker went about his task in the fading light, moths and other insects were often attracted by the lamps causing weird shadows on the packing shed walls. According to Arthur Ball, working in this remote spot in the middle of the woods, down in the valley beside a rushing stream with the odd owl hooting and the noise from the abundant wildlife made him feel rather 'spooky'. He said that during stormy evenings management could not get anyone to work that shift.

David Wills worked on the mine as a young man in the mid-1950's:

Sometimes I worked in the drying sheds - when we were really busy I used to go in at 5 o'clock in the middle of them woods on me own and start work....light up all the burners and get the thing going - light up the old oil burners and they were cantankerous at times to light.... There was no electric down there then, no electric lights not in the actual drying shed. And I was there one morning and I lit up my carbide lamp which the miners used to use underground. And I was rocking the old barrel....used to put the barrel on a thing with a metal bar across under it - you know the size of a beer barrel, well one of those would hold up to 7 to 12 hundredweights according to its size. And they used to put it on iron and then you could shake it.... and I was shaking away and I seen this shadow come right over the top of me and I thought that there were somebody behind me. Course I looked behind me and of course it was the wind blowing the carbide lamp creating me own shadow on the wall.... Made me start for a while but you didn't seem to be afraid of nothing in them days. Course I used to cycle from Christow right into the woods....not many people would go in there today on their own.[13]

All the rail tracks in the mine were 18-inch gauge with the exception of the Crosscut Level and the Launder Level which were 24-inch gauge. The track in the Crosscut Level, along the valley floor and up the incline, was so equipped in the 1930's as the wider gauge allowed higher capacity wagons. The winch serving the incline was an old ship's steam winch worked off the compressed air supply. The whole mill by now was run by only one man who was normally stationed near the primary feed into the system. A wire running up the incline would clang a piece of scrap iron against the shed roof to alert him that a few wagons were waiting to come up. Arthur Ball tells how the winch was rather close to the top of the incline and was not easy to stop quickly. There was more than one mishap as a result.[14]

The other rail system in the wider gauge ran on the level above the mill serving the two Launder Level adits. It was laid alongside the mill launder and on the track of the earlier 18-inch track that used to run back as far as the North lodes. The reason for this larger gauge here in the last 10 years of the mine's life was almost certainly the acquisition of a mechanical rock loader of that gauge and the availability of wagons from the abandoned Crosscut Level. The track served not only a waste rock dump on the hillside, but more importantly, a connection with the mill via No.3 Sawbench Level Main South Lode. To explain this: the train ran to a point directly over the No.3 Level Main South Lode where the tunnel runs into the hill behind the mill buildings. Here, in the fresh air, the contents of the trucks were tipped into a hole in the ground. This ore-pass had a timber chute in No.3 Level below from whence the ore was trammed out to the mill.[15]

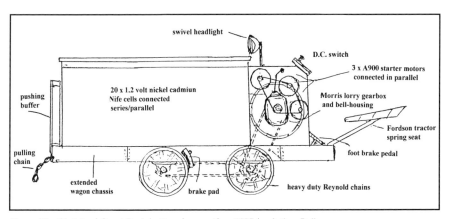

Figure 21 - Sketch of Great Rock battery locomotive. 1957 by Arthur Ball

At that time, in the 1950's, all tramming in the adits was done by hand but the men could only manage one wagon at a time. Mr Taylor, the mine manager, decided that to improve efficiency they should introduce locomotives. The adits were too narrow to take any of the commercially available locomotives. Arthur Ball was therefore asked to create some locomotives himself. The first locomotive (Golden Arrow), built in 1957, was for 18-inch gauge.[16]

The locomotive was battery operated, using starter motors and heavy duty nickel cadmium batteries. **Figure 21**.

It was constructed, to some extent, by trial and error. One starter motor was tried first, then two but this was found to have insufficient power on the gradients, and a third motor was added after a few months, the original batteries being replaced by Nickel-Iron Alkaline batteries. Local scrapyards were scavenged for parts, including the 12-volt starter motors from old Morris lorries. The locomotive was designed with a very short wheelbase so that it could negotiate the tight curves in the adit. **Plate 26, 27.**

Another locomotive (Red Arrow) was built in 1958 for use on the 24-inch gauge line. It was very similar to the first one and had 3 motors from the start. Arthur Ball tells that they were very powerful, and would pull 5 to 6 loaded trucks, and could easily last the whole shift on one charge.[17] The 24-inch gauge loco worked the upper line in Middle

Plate 26 – Arthur Ball, tramming out of Sawbench Level, 1958 with the Golden Arrow. (South Devon Journal)

Plate 27 – 'The Golden Arrow' undergoing maintenance outside Sawbench Level in the summer of 1962. Henry Raisey sitting in the driving seat with designer and builder, Arthur Ball, standing behind (Author collection)

Lode Launder Level, whilst the 18-inch gauge loco ran the length of No.3 Sawbench Level Main South Lode. The Sawbench Level loco was charged overnight in the garage and the Launder Level loco was charged under a crude lean-to cover at the entrances to the level. The Inspector of Mines would not allow it to be done underground due to the venting off of gas, and the danger of explosion. **Plate 28** shows the 'Red Arrow' in its charging shed outside Launder level in 1968. By this time work on Launder Level had been abandoned.

The mine lorry normally used to be left out at Beadon during the day unless it was needed for other jobs. The route back avoided Bell Lane and cut down through what used to be allotments and thence onto the mine road.[18]

Plate 28 - 'Red Arrow' parked in the charging layby close to Launder Level - August 1968
(© M Messenger)

1. Interview - Ron Tucker, 8th April 2002, author
2. Richard Taylor, letter to the author, 5th April 2003.
3. Interview - Arthur Ball, 19th January 1984, C le Marchant
4. Interview - Arthur Ball, 3 May 2001, author
5. Frank Bice Michell, 17 November, 1982.
6. Frank Bice Michell, 17 November, 1982.
7. Henson F. A. On the Occurrence of Micaceous Haematite in the Hennock-Lustleigh Area, Eastern Dartmoor. Proc. Geol. Assoc. Vol 67, 1956, p87-102.
8. Interview - Stan Godfrey, 23 January 1984, C le Marchant
9. Notes by G Bisson, dated 4th May 1954, in BGS archives, Exeter.
10. Kelly Mine Preservation Society Newsletter, May 2002.
11. Report dated 12 August 1957 of visit by G Bisson in May 1957 - BGS archives, Exeter.
12. Loze A. & Lose K., article on carbide lamps in KMPS, May 1998.
13. Interview - David Wills, 23rd January 1984, C le Marchant
14. Kelly Mine preservation Society Newsletter, November 1996.
15. KMPS Newsletter November 1996.
16. Article by Peter Kay - Industrial Railway Record, No.152, March 1998.
17. Kelly Mine preservation Society Newsletter, November 1996.
18. Interview - Gerald Adcock, 25 January 1984, C le Marchant

CHAPTER SEVEN

THE FINAL YEARS 1960-1969

B y 1960, all mining on South Lode had finished and the No.4 Crosscut Level had been abandoned. On the east side of the hill some production was coming from stopes on South South Lode above No.3 level and development and some stoping was taking place on Middle Lode. Much of the production however, now came from the Beadon or west side of the mine. In 1961 it was reported that:

> *South South Lode explored on No.2 and No.3 levels but no connection has yet been made to the drive on the South South Lode from the west (Beadon) side of the hill. Output about 800 tons per year.*[1]

Shortly after this report a connection must have been made between No.3 level and the workings from Beadon Lane as, in early March 1963, the author, with Wensley Haydon-Baillie, climbed through this route.

Whilst underground ore reserves had dwindled almost to nothing, on surface the washing plant had reached a high level of efficiency. The plant could be operated by one man. **Figure 22.**

Run of mine ore was sluiced out of the ore bin across a grizzley where any coarse lumps of granite waste were removed. It then passed to a hammer mill which broke up the soft pieces of high grade material liberating the micaceous haematite. Frank Michell describes some of the processes:

> *The feed then passed through a trommel screen and oversize was jigged (Bennett's 'plunger type screen'). The Hardinge mill was fed with all the stony fractions and the stones in the feed were enough to act as an autogenous[a] feed.[2] After classifying the sand was tabled (3 tables) to separate the pyrite which was hard and ground more slowly than the haematite.[3]*

> *Small amounts of impurities affect the paint making property, for example small amounts of pyrite may decompose and affect the paint –*

---

[a] autogenous grinding uses coarse particles of the material to be ground as the grinding media.

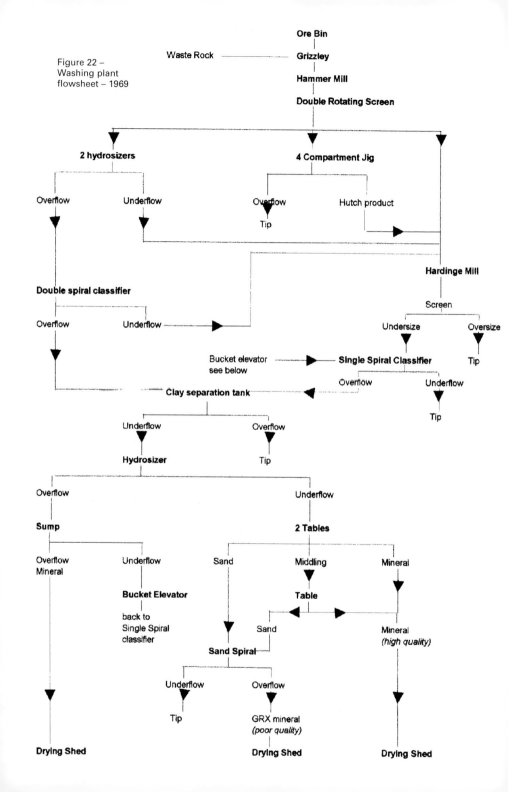

Figure 22 –
Washing plant
flowsheet – 1969

*control was effected in the treatment by changing the 'cut' on the table –
whilst the pyrite tended to be carried up the table to the usual position
(and was rejected) and the sandy fraction found a 'middling' position.
The haematite, when granular reported on the table about the middling
and sometimes could be ground. The finer haematite overflowed the table
due to its shape, the finest fraction of the haematite being mixed with any
kaolin, particularly if the clay was flocculated. I managed to cure this
situation by adding a selective dispersant for the clay and allowing the
haematite to settle more rapidly. Sodium silicate was usually effective
and was added to the final thickener – the overflow contained clay and
the underflow the haematite....*

*Some small (hydraulic) cyclones were introduced....situated down the
valley near the drying sheds and the natural head used to operate the
cyclones. See* **Figure 16**.

*Throughout the process the shape of the haematite influenced the
recovery – some was degradable breaking down into thin crystalline,
micaceous haematite (which is translucent under the microscope – but a
fair amount was hard and could not be delaminated, this haematite
simply ground to a red non-micaceous powder. This harder variety often
came up on the tables and was useless.*[4]

By 1962 carbide lamps had been replaced by second-hand nickel-iron
(NiFe) lamps bought from the National Coal Board. After use, the battery
packs were left charging in a section of the store room, 12 at a time, charging
day and night so that there were always spare batteries charged and ready
for use. The mine foreman used to tend them, checking the electrolyte,
charging them and checking them before being handed out at the start of the
shift. Miners looked after their own headlamps which were attached to their
helmets.

In April 1963 the author briefly worked on the mine as a miner's assistant.
My memories are as follows:

*Labour was collected in the morning by a Bedford van driven by Harry
Penfold. Hours were 7.00 – 3.00 or 7.30 – 3.30 on one shift only and on
a five day week. In 1963 there were 3 working areas: Sawbench Level –
South South Lode (No.3), Launder Level on Middle Lode and a crew on
the Beadon side giving 7 men underground (including myself and
Stephen Atkinson another CSM student). There were 3-4 men on*

surface, Sally Bradford in the office, Billy Wills the Foreman and Mr Taylor the Mine Manager.

My first shift on the mine, a Monday, was typical of my brief period there. I was sent to work on Middle Lode, Launder Level that was being driven west probably hoping to connect with the then productive Beadon development coming east. I worked with Dave Potter – **Plate 29**.

Figure 23 is a composite plan of Middle Lode and the eastern end of the South Lode workings. The section being worked in 1962 was the northerly (shaded) of the No.2 Launder Level adits. The dotted lines on the plan represent horizontal exploratory drill holes. Note how one structure has been followed so far when exploratory drilling obviously hit what appeared to be a more attractive structure to the north. A new drive was then turned off north onto the new structure for a short distance until further drilling identified another better 'lode' yet further north.

Plate 29 – Miners outside the changehouse, 1962. L-R Billy Wills, Stan Godfrey, Arthur Ball, Dave Potter, 'Paddy' Carroll, Gerald Adcock (KMPS collection)

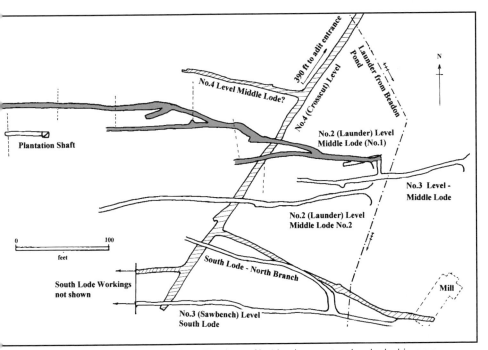

Figure 23 – Plan of Middle Lode workings. The deeper No.4 level crosscut and orebody drives are shown hatched.

Apparently Dave Potter had blasted the tunnel face on the previous Friday so our first task, or so I thought, was to clean the end. There were 3 or 4 side-tipping wagons parked outside the level and a locomotive in its charging bay in a spur near the adit entrance. **Plate 30**

On arriving at the level entrance we found that the loco battery was flat.

"Never mind lad – we'll push a wagon in."

This we did and, after only one derailment, we brought the wagon almost at the end of the tunnel. Within the level clearances were such that the wagon almost touched the sides in places. Standards of tracklaying were poor with the sleepers spaced wide apart and timber sprags jammed between the rails and the sidewalls in order to prevent the tracks spreading under the weight of the equipment. The lode was carried on the footwall side of the drive (South side) and was very erratic. The lode was mainly narrow (sub-economic) with widths of perhaps 2-3 ins. with

Plate 30 – Locomotive and wagon outside Launder Level, 1962. Middle Lode Launder Level is out of the photograph to the left. Tony Haydon-Baillie is standing behind the wagon. (Author collection)

Plate 31 – Chute from Launder Level tramway down to Sawbench Level, 1968. The top of the chute is on the right and the tracks leading away to Launder Level (© M Messenger)

occasional ore shoots where widths increased to 1-2 ft. The lode carried specular iron, some pyrite and micaceous haematite.

Arriving at the end we found a pile of blasted ore across the track and, just beyond this muck pile, an Eimco 12B rockershovel.[b] *Perhaps a further 20 yards in was the face of the tunnel part filled with a further pile of rock. What had happened was this. On the previous Friday, they had temporarily lost one of the wheel nuts off the loader and, as they were so short of ore for the mill, they had blasted some ore down from the roof behind the disabled mucker. Our first task was to release the mucker by shovelling the broken ore from the track into the wagon which we then trammed out to surface. Out in daylight the tracks ran back along the contour alongside the mill launder*[c] *to the orepass.* **Plate 31** *The orepass fed down into a chute in Sawbench Level whence it was trammed out to the mill.* **Plate 32.**

At the top of the orepass a chain had to be hooked onto the body of the wagon to prevent it over-tipping and falling off the chassis and down into the chute. Unfortunately, when we tipped the wagon, the chain snapped and the wagon body, full of ore, tumbled down into the chute

Plate 32 – Locomotive and wagons outside Sawbench Level, summer 1962. Taken on the same day as Plate 27. The wagon bodies shown here were made on the mine
(Author collection)

[b] A rockershovel is a rail-mounted compressed air driven machine designed to load rock into its shovel at the front of the machine. The bucket is then swung over the top of the unit and it discharges into a wagon on the track behind.

[c] This launder ran from a small dam on the Beadon Brook and ran round the contour to the dam above the mill passing in front of both the North Lode and Middle Lode No.2 adits.

below with a splintering crash – watched by a horrified student and a sarcastic miner. It was later hauled out by the mill crew.

Pushing in another wagon we were now able to use the mucker to load the waste pile from the tunnel face. Slide rails were used to extend the tracks into the face. When not in use, the loader was parked in a layby a short way back from the face. The waste rock was similarly trammed out to surface but in this case it was trammed the other way (north) and tipped down the hillside.

"Do we need a chain here?" I asked.

"No" said Dave, "The track is tilted away from the slope and it is quite safe".

"One, two, three – tip"

And over the wagon went and the waste rock poured down the slope. Unfortunately, the wagon body went with it. The last we saw of the wagon body was it bouncing end over end down into the trees towards the explosives magazine. If I had not seen it I would not have believed it.

Once the end was clean it had to be drilled and blasted. Development was carried out in two phases. Phase one involved drilling a number of angled holes from the centre of the tunnel face towards the footwall in the form of a fan cut. This used the softer orebody for the cut and also permitted this part of the round to be cleaned and tipped as ore. Holes were drilled using a jack-leg mounted Holman machine (probably a Silver Bullet). Compressed air was supplied from the compressor which was at the top (southern end) of the mill. The pipe from the compressor was buried and followed the path from the dry (which was just to the west of the mill) to Launder Level adit portal. The piping was about 3 inches in diameter with threaded connectors.

Drilling water presented a problem as there was no water supply underground in the mine. This was overcome by the use of pressure tanks close to the face which were filled with water and pressurised using compressed air. In our case, water was obtained from the mill launder which passed right in front of the adit level entrance. Drilling water was bailed out of the launder using an old paint can and tipped into one of the mine wagons which we then trammed into the level. Because of the poor tracks, derailments were common and in this event the miner pushing the wagon could be deluged with water. This was often of no consequence for if it was the front wheels that derailed and the wagon was in one of the narrow places, one had to climb through the wagon in order to reach the front to re-rail it.

There was no ventilation – only machine exhaust when drilling. When drilling was finished the holes were charged with gelignite and fired using safety fuse. The detonators were supplied separately and had to be crimped onto the end of the fuses before insertion into the explosive. I clearly remember our first blast which consisted of eight holes. We lit the fuses and there was plenty of time to retreat down the tunnel and out into the sunshine before the first shot went off. From out on the hillside we could hear the shots going off one by one. Immediately after the eighth had detonated Dave suggested that we go back in to "see how it has gone". As we neared the face there was so much dust and fumes that we had to follow the tracks on the floor with our feet and run our hands along the walls of the tunnel. As I have since learnt going back into an

Plate 33 – Stan Godfrey drilling in Launder Level – 1962 (KMPS collection)

unventilated end directly after a blast is the last thing that one does as the combination of carbon monoxide and 'nitrous' fumes generated by blasting can be lethal.

And so it went on for two weeks, things really did not get much better. I did eventually get to drive the locomotive and it was surprisingly powerful.

It was not just wagons that went over the tips. On the last day of work before the 1962 Christmas break the team working on Launder Level managed to drive the locomotive off the tracks and down into the wood, **Plate 34**. Perhaps it was a case of Christmas high spirits.?

Plate 34 –
Salvaging the
Red Arrow,
Launder Level,
December 1962
(KMPS
collection)

The main area of production was from what was known as Beadon pit. A winze had been sunk below the lower level on Beadon Lode and a level driven off from the bottom. Reports vary as to its depth, but it was probably 60-100 ft. Tony Haydon-Baillie, who worked there in the summer of 1962 has left us this series of photographs, taken with a basic 'Instamatic' type camera.

Plate 35. Tony Haydon-Baillie drilling in Beadon pit (Author collection)

Plate 36. Hand loading broken rock (Author collection)

Plate 37. Full wagon body at the bottom of the pit about to be hoisted up to Beadon level. Note the ladder on the left and the two rail guides behind the wagon body (KMPS collection)

Plate 38. Tony Bunclarke is about to be lowered down the skip way into the pit. Note he is holding two drill steels in his left hand. This is not how you do it and travelling like this was strictly illegal. The top of the ladderway can be seen in the background. On the left is the hatch cover swung back up against the sidewall. The hatch cover has rails bolted across the top. When a full wagon body had been hoisted up above the floor level the hatch would be closed and a wagon chassis pushed onto the cover below the wagon body. The body was then lowered onto the chassis and the full wagon then pushed out to surface to be tipped down the chute into the lorry for transport round to the washing plant (KMPS collection)

Plate 39. The compressed air winch
used to raise and lower the wagon
body up and down Beadon pit
(Author collection)

The miners working on the mill side of the hill used to come out of the mine and have their lunch in the dry. Sally Bradford in the office would heat up pasties and pies. At the end of the shift everyone was checked out before leaving.

In the later years of the mine's life, when times became hard, the manager introduced the keeping of pigs which were kept in the old staff bungalow buildings which had become run down. According to Arthur Ball, occasionally the pigs escaped into the nearby woods and then some the miners had to come up from underground to recapture them.[5]

In the last years, when mining operations could no longer satisfy demand, micaceous iron ore was imported from Austria.[6]

In the packing shed triple layer brown paper bags (the middle layer bitumen coated for damp proofing) were used extensively for 1 cwt British orders. These were bought printed with 'Ferrubron Micaceous Iron Oxide' logo. Bitumen paper lined hessian sacks were purchased in later years for export orders. One in four were stencil marked at the drying shed by the packing operative. Imports of Iron Oxide came from Austria at approximately 20 tons per month in this type of hessian sack containing a cwt each. This was usually mixed with Great Rock ore (being slightly larger flake ore) and needed to satisfy customer demands.

Plate 40. Full wagon at the portal of the Beadon adit. The wagon would then be trammed to the chute on Beadon Lane for lorry haulage round to the mill. Tony Haydon-Baillie on the left and Terry Bowden on the right. (Apps collection)

On emptying these sacks they were, for quite a while sold as recyclable waste, but later it was decided to re-use them by cutting off the tops straight to contain the 0.5 cwt quantities needed for some export orders (i.e. Australia would only handle 0.5 cwt bags). 1 cwt steel drums with removable clip on lids were used to supply one British customer. Transport to customers were supplied via lorry to Trusham Station or by lorry to the docks.[7]

The market for the mineral was still very much international. For example, on the 16th of September 1965, British Road Services collected 12 tons of 'oxide' for delivery to S.S. Rakaia at No.25 Shed, Albert Docks, London.[8] At that time S.S.Rakaia was owned by the New Zealand Shipping Co. Ltd.. Another load of 10 tons was also dispatched from No.25 shed in November 1968 on the S.S. Gothic outward bound to Wellington and Lyttleton, New Zealand. The Shipping Company for the vessel was Messrs. Shaw Saville & Albion Ltd.[9]

By the mid-1960's the operation could no longer sustain both a mine manager and a mine foreman and Sydney Taylor had to go along with some of the labour. No mine can survive when the lodes underground are exhausted and it is a credit to Sydney Taylor's efforts that the mine lasted as long as it did.[d] The job of mine manager was taken over by Bill Wills. Mrs Devenish, who by then seemed to be in charge of the company, came to the mine about once a month after that.[10]

P G H Richardson visited the mine in the September 1966. By then the labour force had fallen to six – manager, fitter, driver (and loader) 2 miners and a dresser. Adits were then costing about £30.00 per fathom to drive.[11]

Richardson recorded[12]

*As I was about to take my leave, having looked at the mine plans kept in the office, Mr Wills said he had one more thing to show me, and produced a wooden box such as scientific instruments are kept in, with an ivorine tally plate on its lid bearing the words 'The Revealer'. Taken out of the box it proved to be the modern equivalent of a traditional divining rod, consisting of two handgrips, in each of which could be fitted a slender metal rod, graduated along its length, and capable of swivelling horizontally. The two handgrips were joined by a bridge so that they were held a foot or so apart with the rods inclined slightly downwards and (when at rest) parallel to each other, while in the centre of the bridge was a recess in which one of a selection of small glass phials could be inserted. **Plate 41**. There was a rack of about ten of these phials in the box, each marked*

Plate 41 – Bill Wills and the 'Revealer',1968 (© Sunday Independent, Plymouth)

[d] On leaving Great Rock Sydney Taylor joined Coastal Prospecting who were developing an off shore tin dredging operation off the North Cornish Coast near Hayle. Later he became quarry manager at Vyse Quarry in North Devon for Hobbs Quarries, later becoming Divisional Manager until his death in 1976.

as containing a different substance which, Mr Wills explained, would if placed in the recess cause the rods to respond to that same substance if present in the ground over which the Revealer passed.[e] *Response was indicated by the rods crossing each other, the place at which they crossed being a measure of the depth at which the substance might be expected, hence the graduations.*

In October 1967, despite poor results, the labour force was given a pay increase.

As from Thursday the 19th October, all wage rates will be increased by approximately 3%. The old and new rates are quoted below.

Present hourly rate	New Hourly rate
10/-	10/3.5
9/6	9/9.5
8/6	8/9
8/-	8/3
7/-	7/2.5

Signed N A Bennett, Managing Director

By now mining was restricted just to the Beadon side, the old part of the mine was abandoned and the locomotives were no longer used. **Plate 42**

Efforts continued in the hunt for additional sources of ore. A winze was sunk below Beadon Brook from the North level in No.2 crosscut. Also investigated were Shuttamoor and Bowden Hill as the company still retained an option on both.[13] Nothing of significance was discovered.

In April 1969 a letter came from the General and Municipal Workers' Union to Mr Wills.

Dear Sir and Brother

In the absence of Brother Tennant, I visited the mine at Hennock on Wednesday, 2nd April. I had a meeting with our members to discuss their application for an increase in pay. You may be aware that Bro. Tennant did take this matter up with Management but got a very unsatisfactory reply. I understand that Mrs Devenish is visiting the mine on

---

[e] There is no doubt that divining works for picking up things such as buried pipelines, back-filled trenches etc.. Whether it is possible to detect a particular mineral by holding a phial containing the same mineral at the same time is more debatable.

Plate 42. 'Golden Arrow' lying outside Sawbench Level, August 1968 © M Messenger)

15th, 16th and 17th of April and I will endeavour to arrange a meeting with her while she is down here as some of the problems our members are raising ought to be discussed. For your information, our members have elected two Shop Stewards, one for the underground workers and one for the surface workers. Mr S Godfrey ......has been elected to represent the underground workers and Mr A Ball......to represent the surface workers.....

Yours fraternally, G Kirby, District Organiser.

Shortly afterwards, though probably not as a result of the above, the following notice was issued to the workforce on 30th June 1969.

The Ferrubron Manufacturing Co. Ltd.
8 Frederick's Place, Old Jewry, London EC2
Telephone. 01 606 7011

NOTICE TO ALL EMPLOYEES AT GREAT ROCK MINE

The very poor mineral deposits in the Mine now make it completely impossible to continue to operate the Company. It is with great regret that we have to give official notice of termination of employment to all employees.......

For and behalf of
THE FERRUBRON MANUFACTURING CO. LTD.

Marjorie J Devenish – Director

And so mining at Great Rock passed into history.

A final thought from Norman Bennett:

When you see an illustration of the most photographed bridge in the world over Sydney Harbour give a thought to the fact that somewhere in the layers of coatings that protect it is a bit of Devon.[14]

1. Report by G Bisson, 2nd February 1961 – BGS archives, Exeter.
2. Extract from a letter from Frank Michell to Bob Le Marchant, 2nd May 1983.
3. Frank Bice Michell, 17 November, 1982.
4. Extract from a letter from Frank Michell to Bob Le Marchant, 2nd May 1983.
5. Arthur Ball, KMPS Newsletter, June 1998.
6. Norman Bennett in lit., 4 January 1983
7. Arthur Ball, KMPS Newsletter, June 1998
8. BRS collection note, 16 September 1965. K Loze collection.
9. Letter from the Port of London Authority to Keith Loze, 18th February 1974.
10. Interview – Gerald Adcock, 25 January 1984. C le Marchant
11. Notes of visit 9th September 1966 from diary of P H G Richardson copied 2nd June 1999.
12. Richardson P.H.G.. Mines of Dartmoor and the Tamar Valley. British Mining Vol.44, NMRG, 1991 p70-74.
13. Undated letter from R.Hood to P.H.G.Richardson – Richardson Files.
14. Norman Bennett in lit., 4 January 1983.

CHAPTER EIGHT

ACCIDENTS AND NEAR MISSES

Regrettably, like any industry, mining has its accidents and Great Rock was no exception. Some incidents in the later part of the mine's working are recorded below.

Ron Tucker recalls that around 1945/46 there was a fatality to a member of the Tucker family when Bill Coles, the husband of his aunt, was killed by a roof fall when working in a level at Beadon.

He also tells us of another accident some time prior to 1950

> ....when Percy Wonnacott of Hennock almost severed his thumb when working with a Jubilee waggon. He came to the bungalow for first aid (my mum was very good and attended to small accidents). When Percy placed his hand into the bowl to clean the wound the part of his thumb floated to the top held by a slither of skin. My mum was able to reposition and bandage it in place, thus saving the thumb but I understand he could never use it very much.[1]

The Mining Regulations require that accidents serious enough to cause absence from work be officially reported to the local Mines Inspector. These reports are often summarised in a style that seems to be peculiar to Mines Inspectors. From the Inspector's annual report of 1951 we learn that:

> On May 22 1951 at 2.30 pm Mr J A Davey aged 33 was descending a winze when he slipped from the first ladder and when trying to save himself from falling fractured his right humerus.

Shortly afterwards, in 1952, Sam Bradford himself was involved in an accident that could have been fatal. The inspector reported:

> On February 22nd 1952 at 5.30 pm Sam Bradford aged 53 (a drill sharpener). After leaving work realised that the workmen's hut had caught fire, they returned to extinguish the fire when a explosion occurred, probably caused by explosive material inadvertently left in the hut. The man received slight cuts and abrasions to the head from flying debris.

Sam Bradford later described the event in an interview in 1984:[2]

Beadon Bottom? That was where I got blown up. There was a fellow and my brother-in-law was felling timber out Beadon Bottom....he came up one night....

"Sam there is a fire out in the hut out there".

I said "I'll hang on for Bill Hine to come back from Bovey...."

He come back "Oh no, us best go out, Sam"....

I goes up, like a fool I opens the door – BANG – I was lucky because I had cuts around my head....I don't know no more. As it happened the blast went away....it was only a galvanised shed....I didn't know anything about it. Bill Hine dragged me out from there and got me in the lorry and down Bovey Hospital....Mr Taylor came down. Oh he couldn't do nothing, couldn't do anything enough for me. Brought me down cigarettes and all sorts of things.... Bill Hine must have had a job dragging me down out there too and getting in the lorry.

It appears that the miners had left a carbide lamp burning, or a coal too close to the stove, which set the hut on fire. Some explosives, that should have been returned to the magazine, had been left there and the fire detonated it. Sam received no settlement as a result of this accident, and did not make any claim in case it involved any negligence of workmen. Management gave him full pay for the short time that he was off work.[3]

Two years later, in 1954, the Inspector was involved again, when F Adcock (a Cockney Londoner) had an accident.[4]

On May 4th 1954 Mr F.Adcock, who was an experienced stone miner[a] was assisting in altering the position of a bar type drilling machine at the face of a granite heading 6 ft. wide and 6.5 ft. high in a lode of micaceous haematite. Suddenly a stone roughly 6-ins. by 6-ins. by 9-ins. part of a larger slab fell 6 ft. from an unseen clay slip in the roof resulting in a fracture to his right tibia.[5]

After that he worked in the washing plant[6]
Arthur Ball tells that:

Mr Sid Preston, a surface worked doing general duties, once had a broken finger and severely damaged hand caused by an oxygen bottle falling on his hand. He was off work for several weeks and had a wire

[a] The term stone miner is a coal mining term and not one normally used in metal mining. The reason why it is used here is that the Mines Inspector who made the report would have gained his experience in the coal industry. To be appointed an Inspector of Mines the applicant must have held the statutory position of Colliery Manager. In coal mining most work is carried out in the coal seam. A stone miner drives tunnels outside the coal i.e. in the stone.

inserted in his finger to keep it straight. He returned to work on condition he had light duties and was given a job of replacing tram rails underground! David Wills (Nibbsy) helped him and stepped on Sid's finger, causing much pain, but from then on Sid would remove the steel wire in and out with ease.(approx 1955)[7]

Injured miner claims loss of earnings – this was the headline in the Western Morning News for June 27th 1974 when Peter Yeoman, a former miner at Great Rock, was suing Ferrubron Manufacturing Co. Ltd. for damages for personal injuries and loss of earnings since the accident.

Mr Yeoman had worked at the mine since 1956, the accident occurring in 1969 when he was clearing loose rock from a shaft, a rock fell onto his back and there was a gush of water, the next thing he knew he was lying on the ground. When working at the mine he took home £24 or £25 a week but because he could no longer lift heavy objects off the ground and he was not permitted to bend his back too much he had to take other employment assisting a veterinary surgeon in Moretonhampstead at much reduced wages. Ferrubron denied liability, action continued in Exeter High Court[8]

A man said in the High Court sitting at Exeter yesterday that he had suffered a drop in pay of nearly £10/week as a result of an accident five and a half years ago. Mr Peter Yeoman married with 3 children, told Mr Justice Latey that while working as a miner at Hennock near Bovey Tracy he took home £24-25 per week.[9] Peter Yeoman, who was 39, was awarded £5321[10]

Tony Bunclarke had a narrow escape when stoping in the early 1960's

In Sawbench Level....Bernard Hollins saved me....he grabbed me he had only been there 3 or 4 weeks....

I said "look it is pretty dangerous here – stand back"

'Cos we had blasted through like a cave and right down was the drop that was where the winch is....we has to climb up....some metal galvanised chute and in through this little cave and out on the staging and then climb up and there was about 60-70 ft we was working out stoping like.

I was in there charging up and I said to Bernard, I said "Stay back if anything happens just let it go"

I said "There is no chance I get back in here"

....'cos you could hear it letting go, it was wet and heavy like. Next thing I knew was just screaming, punching the wall....Bernard had hold of me shirt. I was just getting out when everything let go. The staging went ladder everything....It caught the end of me boot, crushed me wellie....took my battery and lamp off, but Bernard had reached out and grabbed me....literally saved me.

Another incident, which could have proved fatal, was when Douglas Horrell was gassed in Plantation Shaft. Tony Bunclarke relates:

We was just coming up with the lorry and Jack Payne came running down over. He said

"Come up, Douglas is down the bottom of the shaft, and he's out of his head".

Halfway up he passed out. He went down after they fired the blast[11]

Arthur Ball recalls:

I was at the Plantation Shaft rescue scene. An air hose was turned on to blow out the gas, and a rope passed down the ladderway to tie around Douglas and pull him up.

The miner below shouted up "What kind of knot shall I tie?".

*Mr Taylor replied "Any b***** knot" and I remember shouting "Not a b***** slip knot".*

Bill Hine drove the company lorry across the top fields and took Douglas, accompanied by someone else in the back of the lorry to Bovey Hospital.[12]

1. Letter from Ron Tucker, Kelly Mine Preservation Society Newsletter, November 1997.
2. Interview – Sam Bradford, 17th January 1984, C le Marchant
3. KMPS, May 1997 – Notes from Arthur Ball on accidents.
4. KMPS, May 1997 – Notes from Arthur Ball on accidents.
5. Loze K.,KMPS Newsletter, April 1997.
6. Interview – Gerald Adcock, 25 January 1984.
7. KMPS, May 1997 – Notes from Arthur Ball on accidents.
8. Loze K.,KMPS Newsletter, April 1997.
9. Western Morning News, 21 June 1974.
10. Western Morning News, 22 June 1974.
11. Interview – Tony Bunclark 1983, C le Marchant
12. KMPS Newsletter June 2001.

CHAPTER NINE

PEOPLE OF GREAT ROCK MINE

BY KRIS APPS AND TONY BROOKS

Whilst the story of the mine can be told in bare technical terms, in reality the mine is all about the people who worked there. Their memories and experiences of what happened and what people were like tend not to get recorded yet people remember their time mining for the rest of their lives. This experience sets them apart from everybody else. Below are some memories covering the period 1917 to 1969.

Ron Tucker[1,2,3]
Ron Tucker was 'Young' Charlie Tucker's son and was born in Hennock in 1922:

> *Our mining involvement goes back to my great-grandfather who was a mine captain at a couple of local mines. He also went mining in Cumberland with his two sons Elias (jnr) and Charles. Afterwards he returned to Devon and worked in many local mines, meeting an unfortunate end at Shuttamoor Mine.*
>
> *Elias (jnr) went on to became a mining expert and captain of the gold mines in India. He then went to other parts of the world, including Spain and the Canary Islands.*
>
> *My father, 'Young' Charlie Tucker, went to live with Elias (senior) after his (Elias's) wife died. Elias was living in the village of Hennock on his own and they let Charlie go and live with him for company and it was a matter of a few houses away....lived together until he was 12.*
>
> *My grandfather and his brother often joined in making mining decisions and remained active all their lives. The interest remained and Elias (jnr) was at the Pepperdon mine a few days before he died at 81. Charles remained a consultant to Great Rock and died at 86.*

My earliest memory of visits to Kelly was with my father who around 1929-31 used to drive the Great Rock lorry, taking things to the Kelly mine, or collecting casks of ore for delivery to Lustleigh station. After 1933 my parents moved to Exeter because Mr E M Slatter, the mine owner/manager, bought a car and went to live in Exeter. My dad had to drive him to and from Hennock every day. The lorry driving was taken by Arthur Winslade, a Bovey Tracey man.

Most of my school holidays were spent at Great Rock with my grand-parents who now lived in the mine (office) *bungalow – my grandfather Charles George Tucker* (Old Charlie) *being the general foreman.*

My father took over the management of Great Rock and Kelly after my granddad retired in 1942. I returned to live with them when I was demobbed from the RAF after World War II.

George Stancombe, my mother's father was in charge of the drying and packing shed at Franklin below Great Rock. His home was in one of the two mine bungalows which stood on the site of what is now Great Rock Farm.

What was Old Man Tucker like? *Grandfather like? Great bloke, I think he was – fiery as hell....grandad was happy – quite a happy person....very jovial, liked his drink of course.* **Plate 43**

He didn't learn to drive 'till he was quite old because although he was the first man to own a car in Hennock, my dad drove it and it was the first taxi in Hennock.... I remember Grandad learning to drive in an Austin 7 and then he used to take me with him....I was about 10 or 11 then.... When I left Grandad had a car for work then 'cos he used

Plate 43 – 'Old Man' Tucker outside Sawbench Level, 28 February 1929 (© Tucker collection)

to go to Lustleigh and out to Kelly....he had an Austin 10. He always used to take Tubby Hodge with him, that was his boy, and he would stop at the Palk Arms, have a drink or two, and Tubby was mainly with him 'cos when he drove up past through Hennock and onto the mine there were several gates to open to go through the different fields. Apparently Tubby had got out and opened a couple of the gates and the last gate there Grandad was getting annoyed waiting for him to get back in the car and drive across the field and he said

"Ever seen a car go through a gate, Boy?"

Tubby, of course, said "No"

*"This b***** going through."*

And he just put it in gear and went straight through the gate. He arrived down the mine with bits of gate hanging on the headlights....and poor old Arthur Winslade had to straighten it all up....plus the fact that somebody had to go back, Tommy Sanders or someone, and make another gate.

Another time I remember going with him up on the moor, and he used to put the car in gear, ticking over, and stand on the seat out through the sunshine roof and shoot rabbits....he said he used to do this in India....they had several old vehicles and used to stand on the roof and shoot rabbits or shoot game or whatever there was.

My grandad was a great miner I always thought....he used to show me how you could divine ore or water.

At Ivy Cottage, Hennock, Old Charlie had a blacksmith's shop-garage and workshop – also a field and orchard. Here he kept pigs which were killed on the premises and part shared with the slaughterman and the local butcher. With his blacksmith's skills he was able to sharpen and temper the drills and tools when no blacksmith was available.

Grandad Tucker and 'Lias Tucker were both the old fashioned type of miner ....digging little holes to find things....they were both the same....grandad would say to 'Lias:

"Stick a shovel in the car lets go so and so this afternoon"

And they would disappear for hours....they'd be up Beadon Lane somewhere....what they used to do I don't know but they weren't chasing women like the modern people would be.

What was Edmund Slatter like?
Very quiet sort of man....we used to pick flowers, you know as kids will. I remember down the drying sheds, Plate 44 picking daffodils and you know they always fall to pieces and Edwin[a] would take them from you and strip a piece of bark off a tree and wrap 'em up and tie them....he wan't toffee nosed, he wasn't above anybody, he would kneel on the floor with you and sort of muck about. He would show you things.

I used to remember going out because, Mrs Slatter, although she was not a child lover, she'd always ask you in and give you a drink, me and my brother. And Edwin would lend me his pocket knife or something....or we would go up the woods to Granny's house which was the first bungalow at the top. Up to about 1932 – but he was basically in Exeter then. I found him very nice and his wife.

When she was at the mine....she used to come around that little verandah on the side of the bungalow and ring a bell when she saw a man standing up doing nothing and tell him to get on to work.

After the Slatters moved permanently to Exeter, Mr Slatter arranged the purchase of a house and garage for the Tuckers and paid the deposit. When he died he left his share of the house to the Tuckers and Young Charlie carried on taking Mrs Slatter on drives and shopping on Saturdays.

Plate 44 – Ron Tucker on the bridge by the drying sheds, 1936 (© Tucker collection)

[a] Ron Tucker always refers to Edmund Slatter as Edwin.

We still had the car (an Austin 16) *and this continued till 1942. The car was then commandeered for use as an ambulance. We then moved to the bungalow when Old Charlie retired.*

Sid Preston[4]

Sid Preston must have been the longest serving worker at Great Rock. Born in Hennock in 1903, he went to work on the mine straight from Hennock School aged 13, and he worked on the mine until 1969. He was too young for the First War and too old for the Second so served in the Home Guard. **Plate 45**

I started on 7/6 a week as a lad. It was 3 years before I got 10/-.

Drying sheds
Had a saw bench to saw a lot of wood with the waterwheel....for drying (ie fuel for the drying shed furnace) *and the coal for banking down of an evening or night to keep him going all the night.*

Plate 45 – Top of the incline 1945. L-R Fred Preston, Percy Wonnacott, Bill Hine, Sid Preston, Bill Coles (c Manley collection)

Transport to the station?

When I started there first, horse and cart, they used get the farmer to come in....there was a farmer just a little way at Franklands Farm, chap there, used to go up and get him....they would bring 2 barrels at a time in the horse and cart.

They used to make wooden ladders – light ones when they needed to be moved. Also made ladders with wooden sides and pipes for rungs – heavier for more permanent installations. Candles were used underground when he first went there. They came from Thomas's of Exeter.

Pigs?

Billy Wills used to look after them.... Downfall of the lot. Couldn't do agriculture and mining as well. Used to spend a lot of money on the pigs....didn't marry up together.

Mr Slatter?

Mr Slatter, he was a proper gentleman he was.... He is buried in Bovey Churchyard, we all had to go to the funeral....we were asked to go to the church hall up here and that's where they read out the will. We did not know what was on but we were asked.

The incline up from Crosscut Level?

Many a time winding up wagons and the damned rope broke....lucky didn't have anybody there....wire ropes they used to get frayed out and rust and all that.

When I worked there first, Mr Slatter he used to go and get the money then gradually gave it to the foreman, Mr Tucker used to go and get the money, Lloyds Bank, Bovey Tracey. Then I had to go every week, Fridays to pick up the money....I used to walk....from Hennock, leave just after breakfast and be back by dinner time we call it.

Sid Preston's daughter Beryl (Manley) recalls:

One of the first jobs Father did at the mine was planting trees, I think they were for timber needed down the mine.

He only got £11 a week maximum wages, they had been better off on the state pension than the wages from Great Rock.

Sid's Son, Bernard Preston:

We lived in a green and cream wooden bungalow up the top of the mine somewhere. Dad was employed on general maintenance, a major part of his work was looking after the compressed air system. It was powered by a large single cylinder compressor, I can recall it was so large you could crawl into the exhaust. It had an 8 ton fly wheel, I could remember the weight being stamped on it. The wheel had a counter balance which was barred up to the top to start it each morning.

He also use to maintain the launders, these always leaked, and the shaky tables, which kept breaking down.

The shiny ore use to get everywhere, mother had to wash and scrub his overalls outside before bringing them inside. Even then all our clothes use to sparkle with the dust.

Archie Cudmore[5]

He was born in 1913

The waterwheel used to work everything, there was no expense in the sense of electricity or anything like that or engine or anything. The waterwheel drove everything and the waterwheel worked the compressor. Naturally the amount of speed that the compressor put out depended on the amount of energy that the waterwheel put into it. Whilst I was there they had a little Petter motor installed – to run the compressor

First lorry about 1929 replacing horses.

There was Mr Slatter and Mrs Slatter and they had what you would call an au-pair girl although she was about the same age – Miss Flewin, I think that she was Finnish.

They came out with an idea that being overrun by mice they'd pay me one penny for each mouse tail and Miss Flewin was to count them – marvellous it was.... I would make a heap of them on a shovel and she would take them away and burn them – she never gave me the chance to catch the same mice twice!

Alfred 'Tubby' Hodge[6]

He was born in Hennock. He started as a 'grub boy' and worked on the mine from 1933 to 1939 when he was called up. After the war he worked at Scatter Rock quarry which is not far from Hennock down in the Teign valley.

Mr Slatter?
He was a real gent, Mr Slatter.

Cottages?
Cottages painted green and the inside cream and chocolate.

Silicosis?
Over the years about 20 of these died of silicosis.

Mine lighting?
Candles when first there then carbide.

Shiny ore?
Your best suit – you could wash as much as you like but you went out of a Sunday you always, you always tell anybody worked at the mine – all sparkley....lot of people used to say what that shining on your clothes?

Tom Bellamy[7]

Tom worked at Great Rock and Kelly before the war, starting in 1936.

I'm talking now before the war because I volunteered for the Navy when war was declared. I wasn't actually attached to Kelly mine all the time, when I was needed used to go out from Great Rock, jump on the push bike, go out and do the necessary. I started at Great Rock underground, tramming with Mr Isaacs, then I went stoping with a Mr Bill Miller. When I was needed, Mr Tucker, he was the manager at the time, he used to say would you go out to Kelly. I used to go out to Kelly maybe for a week or so.

My brother-in-law, he was the foreman at Great Rock Mine (Bill Wills) and my father-in-law, which was Bill Wills's father, he worked at the drying sheds at Great Rock. And there was another brother-in-law, he came on after I left (Cliff Wills). Plus I had brothers working there as well.

I can remember when I lived at Hennock, before I left school we had a big bout of silicosis, dozens died, young men. They were drilling dry and it was all that dust from the dry drilling going down clogging the lungs.... I was a school kid but they were young men. I can remember them dying. When I left school and went there it was all wet drilling then.... You get wet but you dress up with oilskins and everything when I was actually drilling.

I lived on the way to the mine, right next to the church. You could see the miners walking by mornings and night times. A lot from Teign Village worked out there. In the evening you would be home from school and you would see them, course the miners used to leave work earlier. I think the miners used to leave work at half past three, the rest of them would be on till about five. At Great Rock I was working mostly underground. When I left the Navy I didn't go back to mining then. I came back to Heathfield open-cast. (This was a ball clay working).

Sam Bradford[8,9]

He was born in Hennock in 1899. He worked in the quarries in the Teign valley before coming to Great Rock, where he worked as the blacksmith. He used to cut and make up the drill steels. Before the days of tungsten carbide tipped steel, the drill steels had to be sharpened and tempered.

Used to cut their own timber out there....used to go out to Kelly, by Kelly Mine, and cut down these big fir trees and get the lorry and bring it back and had a saw out there and used to saw 'im back, you see, for making slabs for making these chutes underground and all that.... We used to cut down a big fir tree up in the woods behind Great Rock and saw 'im down through and make ladders. Used to make what they call old Jacob ladders. They used to cut hitches in them every so often and fix in and nail a rung to stand on....Sid Preston used to do lot of that – 'e was the main man for sawin'.

We used to make all our tool sticks out there....we used to cut down ash sticks and split 'em all out. I used to do them job wet days in the old blacksmith's shop. Make all long stick shovels, pick shafts all had to be done, hammer handles. Used to cut it all out ourself.

Did the Tuckers run taxis?

Yes, they had a taxi service here once. They lived next door to me you know. He was my landlord at one time Old Man Tucker when I just come up here from Teign village....There was the old garage there used to be the old blacksmith's shop.

Pigs?

There was another downfall. When Mr Taylor come here Bill Hine were living in one of the bungalows. Then Bill Hine moved into the old School House and Mr Taylor turned the bungalows into piggeries. Kept lots of pigs. And then consequence were they pigs got out....all over the place and they used to get up in the farmer's fields and then he had miners, who should be underground, out fencing them off with barbed wire....and they went up in Farmer Pearce's place and started on his early potatoes up there.... I believe that they gave him a couple of pigs to hush it up.

Near the end

I was working half-time....and they were going to shut out a lot of the men, stop them. Stopped Mr Taylor, stopped Mrs Taylor, put Billy Wills in charge.

My name....was on the wall to be stopped. Before I was stopped, I was finishing the weekend, I goes out and Billy Wills said "Sam, I could do with you here...."

Mr Taylor come in here the very night he was finishing, and he opened that door and said "Sam" he said "If you goes out Monday morning your job is still there" he said "I've got nothing" and he closed the door and went.

Billy Wills carried on out here until he had to sell up all the stuff out there.....then he had a letter to say 'Services not longer required'.

Rene Aplin (nee Holwill)[10]

She was born in Hennock and lived there all her life. On leaving school she first worked at the Hawkmoor chest hospital. She worked in the mill at Great Rock about 1948/49 for 2 years. She left the mine when she was 20 to get married. At that time she was paid about £3.00 per week.

There was Sam (Bradford)....Sid used to look after the machinery that we worked....Sid Preston. I suppose that was the only 2 men that was outside workers.

All the rest were women?

Yes, washing the ore.

Any young boys?
> *Yes, we did have one young boy, Edwin Preston. He worked there for a while....Bill Hine....was like the foreman.*

In the washing plant?
> *We used to tip into this little square. And you had like a hoe really – a short handle and rake it down and we used to have a hose pipe in one hand. You was washing it with that one and moving it about and after you had washed a nice bit you had real nice grey shining ore looking stuff. And you used to put that in a chute and the rubbish in another chute – sent it out like that. And when they were full, the stone one used to tip into wagons and tip out on the tip, but the black stuff you used to put it through the crush mill. The other washings would down the strips and you had like a spade thing and take it out and keep chucking it up so it washed again and again like. And that used to go right down to the drying sheds.*

Shiny ore?
> *You could never get rid of it.... You'd come home and bath but whatever you done you could always see it sparks....little bits of sparks, you could never shift it*

Sally Bradford[11]
She was born in 1910. She worked on the mine for 28 years up until the late 1960's. She first worked in the washing plant and then, after the war, she worked in the office. Her husband Jack, who was Sam Bradford's brother, worked all his life in local quarries, from 1914 to 1965.

In the washing plant?
> *When the men was in the war I was in the wash box....used to have 2 chutes in there like, one for the stone and we had to play the hose pipe up there....scrape it down and we used to pick the stone out....in two different chutes the stone went in one chute and the main stuff went in the other.*

Did you ever see the directors from London?
> *Oh – saw them all the time....the Secretary* (Mrs Devenish) *she was glamorous, she was, absolutely glamorous she was, and well spoken....and Mr Bennett all them I knew everybody....used to take a tray full of tea when they was there.*

In the office?

> *Used to have a 9.00 o'clock breakfast.... I used to make the tea....used to make the place clean....up the changing house....course towards the end when Old Taylor was a bit more modern than the rest of them he had showers put in.*

> *We used to have some laughs out there but we had to work....it was work, it was dirty.*

The Hine family
Jim Hine

> *We, my sister and I met Charlie Tucker, who was looking for my Dad, (Bill Hine – Plate 46) on the way home from school, we lived in Okehampton then. It was in the war, Dad was not physically fit for the Services, he had had to leave Kelly because of emphysema. Great Rock was very short of miners.[12]*

That was Jim Hine's introduction to Great Rock although he, or more particularly his father, Bill Hine, was no stranger to shiny ore mining. Bill Hine had worked at the mines most of his working life starting at Kelly in 1917[13] when he was 18, previously having been a gardener's boy. In the 1920's and 1930's he worked both at Great Rock and at Kelly.[14] At the beginning of the war he left Kelly and went to Okehampton as he had silicosis but in 1942 he was sought out by Young Charlie. Bill came to Great Rock where he worked as a miner until ill health in 1960 again forced his retirement. At the time there were women surface workers but there were few experienced miners.

> *Several women came to work at the lighter jobs, the first employed starting in 1943. Later in the war the mine became a reserved occupation.[15]*

Bill Hine and his family went to live in one of the mine bungalows. At one time Sid Preston was their neighbour.

> *Water was from springs and contained in a reservoir which is still there, the mine bungalow had a well for their drinking water. There were no other mains facilities, no electricity or telephones. It was far enough from the mine workings to be dust free but even despite washing off down at the mine a lot of shiny ore was bought into the house by my dad, the chair that he sat in would glow in the half light as the shiny ore that was embedded in it sparkled. In those days washing down at the mine was in*

those big deep stone sinks and you washed and hosed down, usually with cold water but sometimes water was heated on the stove to add to the cold. Sometime later, in the early sixties, showers were installed heated by a boiler which also supplied hot water to the mine (office) bungalow but not ours.

As Jim's father was one of the more senior miners he was perhaps given more freedom to go into the mining areas than was allowed to others, he tells:

During the holidays my dad would sometimes take me down to the mine, on one occasion we had to check out a rockfall, we just had one candle light, when we came to the rockfall my Dad left me as he climbed over to check the other side. It was so dark you could feel it, and time seemed to go so slowly. Anyway eventually I heard my dad but as he climbed over the rockfall he slipped, dropped the candle and it was pitch black – luckily he found it and relit it, I was relieved, but it didn't put me off accompanying him.[16]

Jim Hine gained a Scholarship to Newton Abbot Grammar school. In 1948, at the age of sixteen, through his contact with the mines' directors, he was offered a job as a trainee paint technologist with Griffiths Brothers in Bermondsey, London. He also continued his education towards a BSc in Chemistry. Under the tutelage of Norman Bennett the company's chief chemist, and a director of both Griffiths Brothers and Ferrubron, he worked on the testing of ore based paints developed for specific contracts. He was with the company when they transferred to Wolverhampton in 1949 and remained with them until 1952 when he left to do his National Service.

Jim related tales about some of the Griffiths Brothers paint contracts. One was to provide paint for the Sydney Harbour bridge. Another concerned a bridge in Africa:

In 1942 the company won a high profile contract which was later to cause them chemical and financial problems. The contract was to provide paint for the railway bridge crossing the Zambezi river (between Southern Rhodesia and Northern Rhodesia, now Zimbabwe and Zambia). After a few years the paint started to come off. After an on site investigation by Mr Bennett....it was discovered that mites were eating the oil base of the paint just leaving the micaceous hematite which blew off in a fine dust. The bridge had to be repainted using a reformulated paint that now included an insecticide. This incident cost Griffiths a tremendous amount of money[17]

Arthur Ball[18]

He served his engineering apprenticeship at Bridford Barytes Mine, a couple of miles up the Teign valley from Hennock. He started at Great Rock on the 4th of September 1949 and left at the end – 9th of August 1969. His final weekly pay was £29. 5s. 7d. His redundancy pay £814 17s 3d.

Frank Underhill, for many years the drying machine operator, used to air his working shirt over the mess room stove before starting work. One morning his shirt caught alight, and I told him that if he burnt his coat and trousers also, he could claim for new clothes from the firm. Frank thought this was a good idea and set his garments alight. He than asked Mr Taylor, the manager, to proceed with the claim, but was told that the firm did not insure against that sort of claim.... It didn't pay to be dishonest! [19]

What was Sydney Taylor like?
He was a very generous man – if he would do anything to help anyone of he could.

There was never anyone looking over your shoulder over there. They always trusted everyone to do a days work.

Stan Godfrey[20]

He was born in Bovey Tracey. He worked as a miner at Great Rock from 1952-1969, having previously worked at the Blue Waters Lignite opencast mine until it closed. On the closure of Great Rock he went to work in the ball clay pits.

Loader?
We did have one on Launder Level, but it was not all that great....the point was it used to run on the track and if it ran off you had to get the lorry jack to get it back.

How many holes did you drill?
The average used to be on a normal level about 14 to 16....a Vee cut....your first holes would be say about 2 ft. deep and you would put 3 or 4 of these in and your next round 3 ft. maybe and then put in 4 fts.
Plate 46

Plate 46 – Stan Godfrey and M
Burgoyne drilling underground, 1958
(South Devon Journal)

Austrian micaceous haematite?

Towards the end they were importing mineral....from Austria if I remember correctly. the Managing Director, Mr Bennett, said that he had been to these mines in Austria and said that the width of the mineral there you could put double decker buses together.... But the class of mineral was poor, ours is so shiny they's is a dull side like....

Mrs Devenish?

She was quite good she was. Nice? Mm – actually when it finished....she came down and said that was it....broke her heart like, really you could tell by the way she was speaking.

David Wills[21]

Went to work on the mine in 1955, when he was about 21. He worked there for 2 years. Later he worked on the buses as a driver and eventually became an inspector.

Learnt me trade as a butcher to start with....then this job was going and I was interested in lorry driving 'cos I had done a lot of it in the forces and this is what this advertised – lorry driving and general handyman.

Did you work underground?
I have done. I was the spare man, wherever a man was missing I would go like. I worked with Percy Wonnacott **(Plate 47)***, one of the finest miners in this area at that time I would think.*

Taylor?
He was a fair boss as bosses go....quite a nice chap.

Mr Taylor in they days was a Players smoker – used to give us a cigarette every time 'ee seen 'ee would give you a fag – very generous. Had some ups and down with 'ee. I was down in the drying shed....'ee and Arthur (Ball) *passed on the*

Plate 47 – Percy Wonnacott outside Launder Level, 1961 (© John Hamilton, Author collection)

path.....and 'ee said "I'm going down to sack young Dave"....called me young Dave in those days. And he came down....and he gave me a 2d. an hour rise!

The Pond?
The top pond which used to feed the washing sheds with water naturally the filters had to be kept clean and from time to time they used to clean the pond out. **Plate 48**

So this particular day, the Guv'nor said clean the pond out – Sid Preston and me and the boss decided he would help. And in this pond were a lot of fish like and he wanted to keep the fish. So what he decided to do is have

Plate 48 – Washing plant pond, 1950's (photo A Ball, KMPS collection)

some fine gauge wire netting loaded across the brook so and catch the fish and put them back when the pond was cleaned out. So anyhow, he was a very reckless man, nothing could be done quick enough. So he told Sid to go up and open up, and the water started to flow like. But for Mr Taylor it was not fast enough for him and of course there being all this sediment, the bottom part of the hole was choked and he did not give it time to clear. So he said "wind it up some more" so he (Sid Preston) *wound it up some more and all of once it gushed out. Course it gushed out – course it come down the stream and took him with it. And when he got out of the water he was black on one side and he was white the other. Cor, I got in the blacksmith's shop and I couldn't stop laughing.*

Drying Shed?

I fell in the tanks many times. We used to elevate planks over the tanks to wheel it into the shed....I felled off the plank once and went right in the pit.... I was covered in it you know.

Down in the drying shed was a long cylinder that was used to dry – and I would say 12 to 14 feet long and it was a round cylinder perhaps 2 feet high and then there was a lip all the way round it with the actual about 18 inches. I was only thin in them days.... Arthur (Ball) *was the same – and we was the only twos who could crawl inside that drum and when welding had to be done – was bolts inside that needed to be cut, 'tis either him or me that used to go inside – crawl right up in the drum.*

When they were busy – used to fill the tank up and keep pokin' it with a sharp stick then it would go right down solid see and then if you had the time to do this as they wasn't needing the material, you could keep going and get it lovely and you could cut it like cake. But when they were really pushed for it, they start 'en when he was only about a couple of feet high and it would be all like sludge and you would get in the tank and shovel that out and t'was like shovelling jelly out. Then we used to stand on boards and you would float on top of it see and then gradually that board would sink down and you would have to dig the board out to start again like.... Used to lift it to the top of the wheelbarrow from down in the pit, I expect, you know, lift it 6 to 8 feet. And you had that knack of turning the shovel.... When you first went it t'was hard work, but soon as you had that knack of getting it off the shovel there was nothing to it....long handled shovels, very thin in the end you could cut and turn.....

The pick handles, shovel handles, everything was made in the mine, bought nothing. Sam (Bradford) *used to do that. Us would cut the trees down and then went to split then down in fours and cut your handles out from the ends of the trees....everything has to be bought today.*

We used to make our own concrete blocks and everything....for any building work that had to be done any shed be repaired. We used to make our own blocks

Me and Arthur (Ball) *been mates all our lives 'cos we worked in the other mines together – the barytes mines.*[b] *When I left school I was a pay clerk there, worked in the office, and Arthur was a blacksmith....suppose a blacksmith's apprentice or something.... He worked in the blacksmith's shop there....and he was courting at the time.*

The new lorry?
First week we had the lorry..... We used to cut down our own timber for use at home if we wanted logs....the old man would let us borrow the lorry to take it home....and of course Arthur, where Arthur lives, he's got no back entrance 'ev got a front and back door but the back there's no entrance like. So I had a brain idea to go out in the field and drop the

---

[b] Referring to Bridford Barytes mine which closed in 1958

wood out there. Got out there and lost the lorry, sunk right down, brand new lorry, had to stay up half the night to wash 'im off.

Directors?

I can remember the directors coming once....they brought their women with them, their wives. And I had one of the director's cars and took them out for a ride and took them round the reservoirs....and that was people in those days had been abroad and you never heard of many people going abroad in them days 'cos it was a rare thing wasn't it? And they had been to Switzerland, to the lakes, and all that and they said....it was a nice time of the year when the rhododendrons was out....and they said it was the finest sight they ever seen – and they had been to Switzerland..... And I had four wives in the car....the directors was in the bungalow talking business.

What a lovely life that was. T'was good days and the reason I was there was good money.

Tony Bunclarke and Terry Bowden[22]

These two men were interviewed together in 1993, and it has not been possible to separate their individual comments.

Tony 'Bunny' Bunclarke worked at Great Rock between 1955-58 and 1960-69. **Plate 49** Later he went to work in the ball clay mines. Terry Bowden was about 20 when he started mining in 1962.

They describe working on the Beadon side of the mine:

We used the grub hut – got there in the mornings – lit it up (the stove). Came up for breakfast about 10.... put breakfast on the stove, like, in an old tin can on top of the stove to warm it

Plate 49 – Tony Bunclarke with rockdrill, 1962. (KMPS collection)

up. You had your clothes in there. Wills used to drop your dynamite in there, gelignite and used to come out and pick the gelignite up – that what you needed. What timber you wanted, like you know, he would drop in there – you would go out and pick it up.... We used to drive the lorry out under the chute – we used to have the bin filled taken back at night and try to fill the bin again.

We used to have thick canvas trousers, get them wet and they take a week to dry....and when they were wet you couldn't move your legs.

The bin that was out in the road, it was froze one day, we took the lorry out and it was all froze solid. We got the idea of driving a steel bar down through and just putting half a stick of gelignite in just to loosen it up. We blew the chute to bits, the back window out of the cab, and a big dent in the roof. So we worked like hell all afternoon nailing the chute back up, then we rolled a big rock off and wedged it between the tipper and the back window, and we said that's what happened, the rock rolled out and smashed the cab.

I think that the fumes was the worst thing up there after blasting especially clearing the heaps – like dead air – the smell used to come out of the heap of the blasting and give you severe headaches.... I've come home from there sometimes in the evening and your head was sort of splitting....but you go back again. You would go down to the office and get a handful of tablets.

Taylor would give us a few fags "Carry on lads".

*We'd say "We're not going down this b***** place no more, we've had enough".*

He's say "Go home and think about it lads".

Mr Taylor?

He was alright was Taylor, no matter what we done he kept us together like a team....we went overboard heaps of times. His nickname was Edward G....looked like Edward G Robinson.

Carbide lamps?

*Carbide lamps – they were a pain in the **** these lamps. They were if they went out....you could see nothing....everything was wet, so you're* *handling matches with wet hands and the box of matches is wet, can't get a match to light....very often you would find your way in the dark, you would follow the walls all the way out to go outside to get the thing lit.*

We had a front loading shovel – brilliant – when it stayed on the track – came from Cornwall, from the tin mines....only worked on Launder Level.

We were struggling for a long time to find any good lodes, to find anything worth washing really. A lot of addle used to come out for very little ore. You'd be swapping from one level to another, trying to go back on the old seams they'd left years ago. We was looking everywhere come the end for mineral. We were chasing rainbows like, there was nothing in there.

It was fun really – we were youngsters like.

Henry Raisey[23]

He was born in Bovey Tracy. He started at Great Rock on £7 17s. 6d. which was good money in those days.

A new changing shed was built to replace the old one that burnt down. He got about £14 for lost belongings including a coat.

They always wore clogs in the magazine. In the 1950's the magazine was rebuilt to meet the regulations.

Me and Sid Preston....we made the magazine....all inside was wood but have to be brass nails....could have been copper nails....there was always two doors, the first door was wood with two locks on, the second iron door had to be put over smooth so that nobody can get the iron bar in round so they can force it off and there was two big locks. And the walls were that thick (about two feet?). Oh yeah, all that and maybe three....and we put wire netting in there and galvanised....and the top was wired and, oh dear....it was concrete.

Used to charge up last thing at night....Oh yeah that was the last thing we ever done....count the holes....say you have put in say 12 or 18 holes as the case maybe.... one, two, three, four.... You always count them so that you know next morning when you go in (if the miner heard fewer shots going off than he expected this could indicate a misfire).... you have got to be very careful.... The first thing that you do in the morning is go and look for that detonator – don't mind about the dynamite, look for that detonator. If you put a pick in that one and you let that one off....they blow a man's hand off....and you had a matchbox, you cut him off and put him in your matchbox and on the next shift when you do your holes....put him in so he would go off, get rid of him.

In Sawbench Level there used to be old trial pits inside....and there would be boards over them....and all the water running down would go into these pits, catch pits we called them. And every so often we'd clear they out and that would be pure mineral, pure mineral. These pits were about 100 ft in from the entrance to the level.

Pigs?

Oh don't tell me about that, been up there Sundays and Saturdays running after 'em.

I hear that they used to do a lot of damage?

Oh yes, they always took their mouths with them.

Mr Taylor?

Mr Taylor, he was not a bad manager, he would do anything for his men....not all, all depended if he knew 'em.

I enjoyed it....I mean we had some good laughs, we had good fun, better fun, more fun than what is today, oh yes. You never had the money I admit....there was more help in those days.

Gerald Adcock[24]

Worked there up to the end.

Loaders?

They had one. He was a death trap by all accounts....they used to get the pipe tangled up and they could not get to the switch to turn it off and he would run back at them.

Mrs Devenish?

She used to come down about once a month (after Taylor went) *She was fair, she used to say how the finances were going....she was alright, I got on with her very well.*

Christmas time we used to go in the Palk Arms – we got in trouble one year 'cos we finished work early and Mr Taylor, he came back early, we did not expect him by again and he caught us.....He said "I dock it from all your pay packets"...but he never did. He was alright but, how can I put it, he knew the job in theory but he could not do it in practice.

It was a worthwhile job you could see what you were doing.... It was very dirty mind....you could go out with a suit on in the evening, go out and stand under the light and be like a fairy shining.... It got in your skin.... You could never get it out....you change up there, come home and change in the shed, put on clean clothes – it still got in your clothes.

It was a great life up there.

1. Letter from Ron Tucker. KMPS Newsletter, February 1995.
2. Interview – Ron Tucker, 8th April 2002, Author
3. Letter from Ron Tucker to the author, May 2002.
4. Interview – Sid Preston, 17th January 1984, C le Marchant
5. Interview – Arthur Cudmore, 20th January 1984, C le Marchant
6. Interview – Tubby Hodge, 29th January 1984, C le Marchant
7. Interview – Tom Bellamy, Brian Brett, KMPS.
8. Interview – Sam Bradford, 17th January 1984, C le Marchant.
9. Interview Sam Bradford, 26 july 1993 – B Brett.
10. Interview – Rene Aplin, 27th January 1984 by C le Marchant
11. Interview – Sally Bradford, 27th January 1984, C le Marchant
12. From Hennock & Teign Village I remember by W Hine 1977
13. Hine W, 'The Great Rock Mine of Hennock' – Hennock and Teign Village, 1977 p27.
14. Ron Tucker pers comm. January 2003.
15. Hine W, 'The Great Rock Mine of Hennock', Hennock & Teign Village 1977, p27
16. Interview – Jim Hine, September 2002, Kris Apps
17. Interview – Jim Hine, September 2002, Kris Apps
18. Interviews – Arthur Ball, 19th January 1984 by C le Marchant, 3rd May 2001 by Tony Brooks.
19. Arthur Ball – KMPS newsletter August 2001.
20. Interview – Stan Godfrey, 23rd January 1984, C le Marchant
21. Interview – David Wills, 23rd January 1984, C le Marchant
22. Interview – Tony Bunclarke and Terry Bowden. Brian Brett KMPS 1993.
23. Interview – Henry Raisey, 26th January 1984. C le Marchant
24. Interview – Gerald Adcock, 25th January 1984, C le Marchant

CHAPTER TEN

POST CLOSURE AND THE SITE TODAY

A ccording to Norman Bennett,[1] around 1970, after the mine closed, the Ferrubron Manufacturing Company was put into voluntary liquidation. The company records were kept for 5 years by Mrs Devenish and then destroyed.

In liquidating the Company the 102 acres of the mine property together with the mine and all plant and equipment was sold as it stood. The Board, then consisting of Norman Bennett, K.L.Thornbery and Mrs Devenish as Secretary, who was in all but name Managing Director, decided to wind up the company. The company's auditors were appointed liquidators. Norman Bennett goes on:

> I believe the purchaser was a land company which was unknown to me and whose name is completely forgotten. They must be the owners of the mineral rights. I presume it also became the owners of property and rights of Kelly Mine[a] as that mine was not previously sold but just abandoned.

P H G Richardson visited the mine in 1970:[2]

> Not knowing of the closure I had, however, some reason to suspect in 1970 that something might have happened (among other things the mine had gone off the telephone) so decided to make a further visit. This I did in August of that year and found the place deserted and everything in disarray, giving the appearance of having been abandoned for a year or more. Doors were open and windows broken but though some mill machinery had been removed most of it was still there. A union card for S. Tremain lying on the floor of the blacksmith's shop showed his last deduction to have been made in February 1969.

In October 1970, the remaining plant, was being dismantled and taken away, though the tables and ball mill still survived intact. **Plate 50** – In the foreground is the Hardinge mill, centre back, part obscured by the steel joist,

---

a Kelly was not owned by Ferrubron. On final closure the land and the rights reverted to the owner, the Amerys of Kelly Farm.

is the revolving screen. The drying shed had somehow escaped the attentions of the scrap dealers up to that time, though in due course it was cleared and demolished.

Plate 50 – Demolition of the mill, 1970 (© P H G Richardson, Totnes)

Plate 51 –
Great Rock
mine wagon
in
Okehampton
Museum,
1998
(© Author)

Not all of the mine's equipment was scrapped. Mr Robin Hood rescued some of it which was subsequently given to the Museum of Dartmoor Life in Okehampton.[3] This includes a wagon from Sawbench Level, some tools and the shell of the Hardinge mill. **Plate 51**

In May 1993 Devon County Council issued the following letter:[4]

Order Prohibiting the Resumption of Mineral Working, Great Rock Mine Hennock

The Secretary of State for the environment confirmed the Prohibition Order on the 19th April 1993 with some amendments to the original wording and a replacement plan. The Department of the Environment has requested that copies of the Order are served on the owners and occupiers of the land to which it relates, and on any other person who will be affected by it. I therefore enclose a copy of the confirmed Order and plan.....

In 1994 the woodland containing the mine was for sale for £42,000.

The Mine Today (2002)

All of the workings and structures described below are on private land.

The underground workings should only be explored by groups with recognised mining experience <u>and</u> with the permission of the owners. Unauthorised breaking into gated workings is a criminal offence.

The underground workings at Great Rock can be seriously dangerous where driven on lode. As previously described the overhand stoping method involved leaving the waste rock on timber stulls in the stopes above the levels. With time much of the timber has rotted and it is only the waste rock in the narrow stopes jammed together that prevents the whole lot from dropping out. An additional hazard lies in the floor of some of the levels. In several places the lode has been stoped away below the floor of the level. The resulting pit is sometimes open and often flooded, having been simply boarded over some time in the past.

The Beadon Lane (western) part of the mine

Starting from Chericombe Cross, Beadon Lane falls away downhill in an north-westerly direction. After about half a mile the waste dump from South South Lode can be seen on the right hand side of the lane. A track has been bulldozed off the road at this point and crosses in front of the lower adit mouth. This adit is open as far as the first stoping where the stulls have collapsed blocking the level. Just back from the collapse are the remains of the ladderway and skipway from whence the ore below this level was stoped and hoisted. **Plate 52** – Note: the ladders have been removed from the manway, but the skipway rails to the left still remain. Eventually these lower stopes connected with the South South Lode workings on No.2 and No.3 Levels.

Plate 52 – Stope below Beadon South South Lode level, 1976 (© Burt collection)

The next item of interest further down Beadon Lane is the remains of the loading chute from the Beadon Middle Lode adits. There is a large waste dump here and the shell of the grub hut still stands outside the adit entrance. This was one of the last sections of the mine to be worked and it was from this level that the Beadon Pit was sunk. The level is open as far as the first stopes where the broken stulls and waste now block the level. Both this adit and another one further up the hill are gated.

The final workings are on Beadon North Lode near the bottom of the hill. There are the remains of a loading chute by the road and two levels up the slope. There is limited stoping on the lower level which is open to the end. Both adits are gated.

At the bottom of the hill Beadon Brook passes under the road. About 100 yds downstream from the bridge is the Beadon pond. Whilst the pond is now severely silted, up the dam wall and spillway are very obvious. This dam fed the wooden launder that ran around on the contour to the washing plant. In the late 1970's much of the woodland, previously owned by the mine, was felled and the area planted with conifers. At that time the launder

128

was destroyed when the route taken by the launder was bulldozed to provide access for logging machinery.

The mill or eastern part of the mine

Following the track from Beadon Lane smashed fragments of the launder can still be seen in some places. After about half a mile the gated entrance to the lower of the two North Lode adits can be seen on the right. From here a tramway ran alongside the launder to the washing plant. North Lode workings are open throughout and stable. In the 1970's and early 1980's they were used by Leicester University Geological Department for field work.

A little further along the launder track, just after the track swings to the right are the two gated adit entrances on Middle Lode. The second adit is very short, but the first one extends well into the hillside and is open to the end. This is the level where the author worked in 1963. **Plate 53**, this is fairly close to the end of the level and is where the author found the air operated loader on his first shift on the mine.

Just before the Middle Lode adits a forestry track swings off sharp left back down the hillside below the North Lode waste dump towards Beadon

Plate 53 – Chute and ladderway, Middle Lode Launder Level, 1976 (© Burt collection)

Brook. This leads to the Crosscut Level. This 'new' track crosses in front of the adit portal partially damming the gated entrance. **Plate 54**.

Plate 54 – Entrance to Crosscut Level, May 2002 (© Author)

From an exploration point of view, Crosscut Level is the safest and one of the most interesting of the levels accessible at Great Rock. The crosscut is driven straight in for about 700 ft. with workings which roughly correspond with North, Middle and South lodes driven off it to the west. The majority of lode development is on South Lode driven west off the end of the crosscut. There is limited stoping and the level has survived very well. Just to the west of the main crosscut is the first stoping. The author, pictured here in the centre by the first chute, has been captured in explanation mode. **Plate 55**.

Access westwards is open to the point where the main ore shoot has been mined through to No.3 level above. Further progress is impeded by a flooded stope below the floor. There is no further stoping beyond this point and the level is open to the end. Outside, Crosscut Level has a large waste dump running along the valley downstream and towards the bottom of the incline up to the washing plant. Below the dump at stream level is the storage pond which was used to augment the water supply to the drying shed. The pond is now dry. The incline itself is badly eroded, overgrown and is difficult to interpret.

Plate 55 – Chute on South Lode, Crosscut Level, author in centre, about 1990 (© A Bromley)

Just below and upstream of the Crosscut Level portal there is a small dump. It is believed that this was from a short adit driven on River Lode. The entrance appears to have been obliterated by the logging track previously mentioned.

Returning to the launder track, the waste dump from Middle Lode can be seen at the top of the track up from Crosscut Level. Directly below, in the trees, is the remains of the explosives magazine. From the Middle Lode adits the tramway ran for about 50 yds to the tip where the ore was dropped down into Sawbench Level for re-tramming to the washing plant. Today there is no sign of the tip. The forestry/launder track continues on and joins the main access track from Hennock into the mine. The header pond which fed the washing plant lies just above the access track and still holds water.

The track from the pond drops steeply down a short hill and then swings sharp right onto a level area that once was the centre of the mine. This area is now part of the grounds of a private house. On the far side of this level area the buildings that once served as the sawmill, workshop and garage still exist and are largely intact. To the left of the end of the access road is the entrance to Sawbench Level, now almost hidden in vegetation.

From the industrial history point of view, Sawbench Level is the most interesting level on the mine. When the mine was abandoned this level escaped the attention of the scrap man. When I first went back to Great Rock in 1983, apart from one roof fall, the level was open right along South Lode and through the crosscut to the end of South South Lode. The pipes and

131

Plate 56 – Wagon in No.3 Level South South Lode, 1983 (© J Watton)

Plate 57 – Water pressure tank, No.3 South South Lode, 1903 (© J Watton)

equipment were still in place and it was as though the miners had just left. Trapped beyond the fall there is one of Arthur Ball's mine wagons, **Plate 56**.

Near the end of the South South Lode drive is a pressure water tank **Plate 57**. Note the old tin used to fill the tank. Derek O'Sullivan on the right.

Just beyond the pressure tank the skid rails from a flooded winze protrude through a pair of trap doors. **Plate 58** – The trap door has been pulled back to the right exposing the flooded winze down into the stoping.

A Holman compressed air winch, which used to hoist from this pit, stands in an alcove on the far side of the winze. **Plate 59** The author provides scale.

Over the years the level has become progressively more dangerous and there have been several further falls where some of the stope fillings have dropped out. **Plate 60**. This is a particularly high section of Sawbench level. Note the way that the timbers are hitched into the footwall (right) side of the drive and then just hammered down on the hangingwall (left) side. The planks above the cross-timbers are holding back the discarded waste in the stope above.

Outside Sawbench Level the washing plant has all but vanished and only a few concrete foundations survive. Slatter's mine bungalow is now a private house and looks just as it did in the 1940's, **Plate 61**.

Plate 58 – Winch and skip-way, No.3 Level
South Lode, 1983 (© J Watton)

Plate 59 – Winch, No.3 South South Lode, 1983
(© J Watton)

Between Sawbench Level and the bungalow the grub hut/change-house has survived intact and today is used as an office and as a store.

Up the hillside in the trees above Sawbench Level and the launder track are the gated portals to No.1 and No.2 levels on South Lode. In No.2 level, once past the orepass that drops down to No.3 level, the level is open as far as a roof fall at the first stope. The exploratory crosscut south to South South Lode is open as is the drive on South South Lode. There is no stoping here. There are indications that this fall in No.2 and the original fall in Sawbench Level were caused deliberately. When I first saw these in 1983, both of them had what appeared to be electric detonator wires coming out of the rock piles. Now these are old stopes and all production blasting here would have been done using safety fuse. I have no knowledge as who did it or why this was done.

Almost at the top of the hill above the Middle Lode adits is Plantation Shaft. It is open (May 2002) and securely fenced. There is a small waste dump running along the contour to the South and two rusting wagon bodies. In the shaft the skip-way rails can still be seen.

Plate 60 – Detail of timbering below an area of stoping, No.3 Level South Lode, 1983 (© J Watton)

Plate 61 – Mine office/bungalow, 1983 (© J Watton)

Plate 62 – Old launder to drying sheds, May 2002 (© Author)

Drying Sheds

The path from the washing plant down to the drying sheds has all but disappeared, however odd pieces of the old launder still stand amongst the trees. **Plate 62**.

At the site of the sheds the foundation of the main building is still visible. The settling pits are very overgrown and are just discernable amongst the trees. There are a further 2 pits on the stream side. Looking at the site today (2002) it is difficult to imagine that this was a centre of industrial activity less than 40 years ago.

The Future?

And what of the future, will the mine ever be worked again? The answer must, sadly, be no. There are, I think a number of reasons for this.

The most obvious is the complete absence of any visible ore reserve. There may be other, as yet, undiscovered lodes but even to be considered today they would have to be at least as good as the Main South Lode, which was the most productive micaceous haematite lode ever worked in Devon. Narrow lode mining is almost impossible to mechanise and the mining method would have to be much the same as used previously, that is if modern regulations would permit it. There has been very steep wage inflation over the past 40 years and today the relative labour costs would be much higher, if men could be found to do the work.

Secondly, there are planning and environmental restraints. As the mine lies in the Dartmoor National Park it is unlikely that planning permission would be granted, no doubt on the grounds that it would cause landscape damage and change. If permission were to be granted it would demand that, at the end of working, the site be "restored" to its former condition. Yes – mines when they are working do make an impact on the landscape with buildings and waste tips. But yesterday's industry is today's archaeology and are places of interest and biodiversity. For example, old mine workings are one of the major hibernation places for some of our rarest bats; some mine dumps are now Regionally Important Geological Sites (RIGS).

No one in their right mind would suggest that the valleys of Dartmoor that have been turned over by the tinners should be landscaped and restored to their former condition, that the old dry leats should be obliterated or that the stone rows and hut circles be cleared away! Dartmoor is the more richer because of their very existence. We live in a man-made landscape which is a reflection of our past, a past which ended yesterday. We all want our bag of cement, pack of nails or perhaps a can of rust resistant paint, providing that the raw material is extracted somewhere else!

1. Norman Bennett in litt, 4th January 1983.
2. Richardson P.H.G.. Mines of Dartmoor and the Tamar Valley. British Mining Vol.44, NMRG, 1991. p70-74.
3. Western Morning News, 27 November 1984
4. Letter to Mr and Mrs Apps, Twizzle Tree Cottage (the old mine bungalow) dated 11th May 1993.

CHAPTER ELEVEN

HENNOCK VILLAGE – THE INFLUENCE OF MINING ON THE COMMUNITY

BY KRIS APPS

S o what sort of village was Hennock when mining re-started at Great Rock
in 1896?
Hennock is an old village with an 11th Century tithe barn, a long-house,
a 14th Century church and a Victorian vicarage. In its time the village has
formed part of the manors owned by Torre Abbey and later, after the
dissolution of the monasteries, it was owned by Sir Lawrence Palk after
whose family the Palk Arms is named. It has developed as an industrial
village where once mining and quarrying, along with agriculture, were the
major industries. Over time cottages have been added to the village and
replaced by larger terraced housing. At one time there were three licensed
premises in the village: the Palk Arms, its immediate neighbour the Union
Inn and at the other end of the village a cottage licensed for selling ale. There
were travelling salesmen, hawkers, an established shop and a bakery. There
is an assortment of houses, small farms and country houses, old terraced
cottages and post war council housing. Now expansion of the village is
limited as the village falls within the Dartmoor National Park and is not
designated for development.
Throughout the second half of the 19th Century agriculture was
important employing between 29% and 62% of the male population. Mining
and quarrying also played a significant part in the community's economy
employing between 20% and 36% of the working males. The miners were
mainly employed in the lead and zinc mines in the Teign valley at the
Frankmills, Exmouth and South Exmouth (Hennock) mines which worked
between about 1850 and 1880.[1] As we have seen in Chapter One, in 1881, 11
men were employed in the iron mines. The village also had many tradesmen
whose livelihoods depended on these industries including blacksmiths,
carters, and masons. Mining also brought 'foreigners', miners and
tradesmen from Cornwall and the Tavistock area of Devon, unlike most
agricultural villages who drew their communities from the immediate local
parishes. The 20th Century saw the re-opening of Great Rock, and for the
next 60 years the mine was an important part of the village's economy.

The importance of mining in Hennock in the 19th Century

Population figures used here for Hennock includes all those living within one mile of Hennock church. A glance through the census for 1851, 1871 and 1891 gives an indication of the types of people who lived in the village and the changes which occurred over the latter half of the nineteenth century. To show the importance of mining to Hennock during this time the data for Hennock is compared with the national trends in Britain.[2]

Table 1
A comparison of the percentages in the occupational divisions for 1851, 1871 and 1891.

	Hennock			Britain		
	1851	1871	1891	1851	1871	1891
Trade	31	26	26	10	13	16
Agriculture	42	29	62	22	15	11
Mining	22	36	0	4	5	5
Others	5	9	12	64	67	68
Number of working men in Hennock	72	65	60			

The heading 'trade' covers skilled craftsmen such as carpenters, masons, millers, bakers, blacksmith and shoemakers(cordwainers); 'others' incorporates a diverse range of occupations from publican to cleric and includes landowners who consider their occupation to be other than farming.

Mining and agriculture only specifies the numbers directly employed in those industries, however they will probably employ tradesmen such as blacksmiths and carpenters. The isolation of Hennock meant it was important that the village had the necessary craftsmen.

Looking at the occupations of working males in 1851 22% were involved in mining, by 1871 this had risen to 36% replacing agriculture as the main occupational yet by 1891, 12 years after the collapse of lead prices, there were none. Although there was a reversion to farming contrary to the national trend indicated by Dean and Cole[3] the actual number of workers had fallen.

The fact that by 1891 there were no active miners left in the village appears to substantiate a statement by Schmitz[4] that the decline of the mining industry resulted in a reduction of the population.

Table 2
Hennock district population changes 1801-1891 (after Schmitz)

Date	1801	1811	1821	1831	1841	1851	1861	1871	1881	1891
population	537	575	678	747	828	894	1004	887	769	685

Cornish Incomers

The population of Hennock from 1851-1901 is notable for a relatively large number of Cornish incomers compared with those from other parts of the British Isles. Comparing Hennock with nearby Chudleigh Knighton, a ball clay cutting and brick making village, both villages had a sprinkling of incomers from other areas, and a substantial amount of movement into the villages from other parts of Devon. Those from out of county were either professionals such as clergy, teachers, engineers and pensioners with their own means; those from within the county were either craftsmen or semi-skilled labourers.

The Cornish were the exception. The majority of these were connected with mining. Others included a carpenter who may well have come to Hennock as a mine carpenter, a miller and a certified teacher and her mother. None of these appear to be related to any of the Cornish families living in Hennock but may have been known to them before their arrival in Hennock. It is also clear that most of the out of county incomers did not spend long in Hennock. With a few exceptions where miners raised families, miners only appeared in a single census and were not found in the neighbouring census areas afterwards.

Cornwall exported mining expertise in the form of miners, engine drivers, mine agents, mining engineers etc.. It is interesting that all but one of the Cornish mine workers classified themselves as miners including 15 year old boys. In contrast the girls, aged between 14 and 20 were classed as mine girls or mine surface workers (1871 census). Amongst the mine workers born in Devon most, including Elias and Charlie Tucker, called themselves mine labourers although they were in fact experienced miners or mine captains.

Table 3 shows the importance of Cornish miners to mining in Hennock and probably to mining throughout the Teign Valley in the Nineteenth Century. From the census it was also found that miners born in other areas of Devon living in Hennock had children that were born in Cornwall and some of these children became miners too. The exact number is hard to tell as few of the boys appear again in the census of our area after the age of 16. Mining was not so ingrained in the Hennock born population as under-21 year olds working as mine labourers were found in later census working as general labourers. Also of note is the fact that 50% of the non-Hennock born miners from Devon were born within a few miles of Tavistock which was Devon's main mining centre.

Table 3
Origin of Miners living within one mile radius of Hennock Parish Church

	Hennock	Devon	Cornwall	Other	Total
1851	2	1	9	1	13
1861	27(*3)	11(*2)	15	1	54
1871	18(*2)	8	16	0	42
1881	5(*1)	2	6	2	15
1891	0	0	0	0	0
1901	2	2	0	0	4
	54(*6)	24(*2)	46	4	128

*includes children of Cornishmen

With closure of the lead mines and the apparent cessation of iron mining, the 1891 census showed no miners living in the village. There were also very few Cornish remaining, those that were had been long standing inhabitants. There was Jane Fragle, a miner's wife, now a widow, who had spent most of her adult life in the village, appearing in all the census 1851 to 1891 except 1871 and Henry James, a former miner and now, in 1891, a labourer. He was the only one left from a family which had moved to Hennock prior to the 1851 census.

One Cornish family did stay in Hennock. Mathias Jole from Stoke Climsland and his family were first noted in the 1871 census, Mathias as an engine driver, probably a mine engine, and William, his nineteen year old son, as a miner. That is the last mention of William, but Mathias, his wife and his daughters remained in Hennock for the rest of their lives. By 1881 Mathias had become a tea dealer and pedlar. In 1891 now as Matthew Jole he had become a tea dealer and draper and in the last published census, 1901, he had become a grocer with a shop in which his wife and unmarried daughter worked. That shop closed in the late 1990's and has recently been turned into a house with the removal of the shopfront window. With its closure, Hennock lost its only purpose built shop. His other daughter lived close by and her husband, George Simmons, carried on the Jole family business as a tea dealer and draper. His grand-daughter, the eldest of five, was a pupil teacher in Hennock school. By 1901, apart from the Jole family, the only other Cornish person was a young farmer's wife living at Longlands Farm in the centre of the village.

The professional incomers did not appear to have remained in the area for very long and none appeared in more than one census. These professionals were drawn from as far afield as Cumbria and Middlesex, and on the whole they were either single or had no family. Chudleigh Knighton differed from Hennock in that there were several in domestic service from out of county staffing the homes of non-Devonians. This mobility was also true for most of the mine labourers under 21 born or living in Hennock as children. It did not seem to matter where one was born, most youths seemed to leave Hennock once they were of an age to work.

Table 4 No.s of children under 14 in Hennock				Table 5 Occupations of 10 to 13 year olds			
	1851	1871	1891		1851	1871	1891
10-13	14	15	17	scholar	6	9	13
6-9	53	40	17	working	3	5	2
2-5	48	40	27	nothing	5	1	2
under 2	27	20	17	totals	14	15	17

Table 4 lists the relatively small number of children in the 10-13 age range compared with the 6-9 year old and the 2-5 year olds and suggests that many left the village to work. **Table 5** shows the number of scholars in this age range does increase, presumably as a result of the 1870 Education Act. Both boys and girls were employed as mine surface workers. Others worked as domestic or farm servants. There appeared to be an increase in those attending school with two girls classed as teachers in 1871 and 1891

Family Sizes

Family sizes were varied, but it is difficult to ascertain the size in the 1800's because so many children worked, and they worked away from home. The youngest living away from home was John Heath, aged 8, classed as a farm servant. Elsewhere in the village was 22 year old Sam Heath, also a farm servant. Villages like Hennock did not have house numbers and unless a house was named on the census like Lakes Farm cottage, most houses in the census came under the heading 'village'. It is also difficult to trace family size from the parish records.

There were often many with the same surname making it difficult to trace which family young workers belonged to. It was not only the surname which was the same but also the christian name, as children were named after their parents, aunts and uncles meaning that cousins often carried identical names and were often much the same age. This was particularly true among agricultural workers and to a lesser extent amongst the miners.

Throughout the last half of the century agricultural workers showed an increase in household size but a reduction in the number of children per household living at home, whereas farmers showed a decrease in households of 6 or more, from 75%, 1851 to 14% (1891) and an increase in the households without children.

A farmer and tradesman might be able to afford to keep his family at home, and have the space to do so. Agricultural workers could not and their children may have left home at twelve or thirteen to work as agricultural servants and domestic servants. These figures represent the number of children the household could support although there were not so many young farm servants by 1891. A household gives no intimation of the rooms available until the 1891 census, but there was a tendency for miners to have unrelated lodgers from their own occupation. Craftsmen and tradesmen also showed a trend towards smaller households but they tended to have larger families.

Labour at Great Rock

Whilst Cornwall was an important source of mining labour in the 19th Century, this was not that case when Great Rock re-started about 1900. The Cornish mining industry had been in decline from about 1850 and over the next 30 years there would have been many out of work miners desperate for employment and, as we have seen, some of them came to work in the lead mines in the Teign valley. However, by 1900, whilst relatively few Cornish mines were working the labour situation had changed. Miners who were prepared to leave Cornwall could earn exceptionally high wages in the South African gold mines. In 1902 there were more Cornish miners working in South Africa than in the Cornish tin mines.

We have no comparative census figures, however it is apparent from the interviews for this book, that most of the men were born locally and joined Great Rock having had no previous mining experience. You only have to look at the list of names, Tucker, Stancombe, Preston, Sampson, Wills and Potter; there were fathers and sons, brothers, uncles, some times three generations of a family worked there. There were marriages between the families. Unlike mining in the early days Great Rock was a local mine with most of the miners being local lads.

1. Burt R. et al., Devon and Somerset Mines, University of Exeter Press, 1984.
2. Dean & Cole (1967) Communities and Families, edited by John Golby, Cambridge University Press. 1995
3. Dean & Cole (1967) Communities and Families, edited by John Golby, Cambridge University Press. 1995
4. Schmitz C. J., The Teign Valley Silver-Lead Mines 1806-1880 (2nd Impression) Northern Mine Research Society, Sheffield. 1980

CHAPTER TWELVE

THE MICACEOUS HAEMATITE VEINS OF NORTH–EAST DARTMOOR

BY R.C. SCRIVENER, BSC, PHD, CGEOL, FGS

The granite of north-east Dartmoor, in essence that part of the outcrop lying to the east of the Sticklepath – Lustleigh Fault Zone, is noted for the occurrence of numerous veins bearing haematite as their major constituent. **Fig 24** In particular, those veins between Hennock and Lustleigh are re-markable for yield-ing micaceous hae-matite, a fine-grained variety of grey haematite. Most of the veins also carry some hard, granular spe-cular haematite, and this variety is predominant in veins occurring to the north and west of the micaceous oxide district. In the central part of the Dartmoor Granite, specular haematite occurs together with cassiterite and tourmaline in the tin mining district of the Birch Tor and

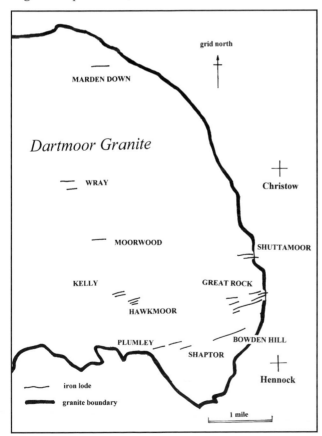

Dartmoor Granite

grid north

MARDEN DOWN

WRAY

Christow

MOORWOOD

SHUTTAMOOR

KELLY

GREAT ROCK

HAWKMOOR

PLUMLEY

BOWDEN HILL

SHAPTOR

Hennock

iron lode

granite boundary

1 mile

Figure 24 – Micaceous Haematite Lodes of North-East Dartmoor

143

Vitifer mines, and in the Chagford area. The specular haematite is too hard to be ground for use in paint, and is not found in sufficient quantity to have been mined for smelting.

Host rock

The haematite veins occur in the Dartmoor Granite, which was emplaced at the end of the Variscan Orogeny, a period of intense tectonic activity, that resulted in an episode of mountain building towards the end of the Carboniferous Period. The Variscan tectonic activity, essentially the result of a collision between two convergent continental plates, resulted in large-scale melting of the lower part of the crust beneath the area that is now SW England. Extensional faulting in the aftermath of this collision permitted the molten magma to rise upwards and crystallize at relatively shallow levels in the crust. These bodies of crystalline rock were subsequently exposed by erosion, and today form the outcrops of the various granite plutons of Cornwall and Devon.

The largest of the granite plutons is that of Dartmoor, which insofar as its northern part is concerned, was emplaced at 280 Ma (million years before the present). The granite is a coarse-grained rock formed from feldspar, quartz and mica, commonly with locally abundant large porphyritic crystals of potassium feldspar (perthite) up to 10 cm or more in length. These form a striking feature of the granite. The variety of mica present in the granite is mostly biotite, an iron-rich variety, though muscovite (white mica) is also present in places. Aggregates of the borosilicate mineral tourmaline (variety schorl) are scattered throughout the granite, and in places tourmaline has replaced considerable volumes of the primary granite: it is also present in veins. While most of the granite seen at outcrop in NE Dartmoor is the coarsely porphyritic biotite granite (known informally as the 'giant' granite), there are also numerous sheets of fine-grained pink or pale grey granite (aplite), generally biotite-poor, but rich in tourmaline.

Vein structure

The haematite veins cut through, and therefore post-date, the coarse granite and the later aplite sheets. On geological maps, such as the published British Geological 1:50 000 – scale Sheet 339 (Newton Abbot), the mineralised zones or 'lodes_ are represented at outcrop by heavy lines of roughly east–west trend, which suggest a regular series of tabular orebodies. This shorthand, while necessary and convenient, in fact belies the complex structure of the lodes. At Great Rock, the surface outcrops of the lodes trend (strike) between 070° and 080° and are traceable for up to 850m. Individual veins are inclined (dip) at steep angles to the north, and in places are nearly vertical. Typically, a lode comprises a swarm of veins and veinlets, which are mostly parallel or subparallel, but in places coalesce. The vein zones may be several metres in width, with components varying from millimetre-scale stringers to workable orebodies up to 1.2m wide. The lensoid form of the orebodies, with irregular pinching and swelling, accounts for the complex stoping patterns seen on the various mine plans.

Throughout Great Rock and the other haematite mine workings of the district, individual veins show strongly developed grooved markings or 'slickensides' on their walls and within the vein fillings, indicating relative movement, generally in a vertical sense, of the enclosing granite. This is good evidence that the veins originated as faults, and the presence of slick-ensides within the vein fillings suggests that movement of the faults persisted after deposition of the ore. The lodes are cut in places by later faults, mostly minor, and generally of north-south trend (crosscourses); these are barren and commonly filled with clay or brecciated granite. The displacement along these late faults is usually small, although some larger examples exist, for example in the Bottom Adit of Kelly Mine.

Vein mineralogy

The haematite worked for use in paint consists of steel-grey plates in the size range 10 to 200 microns, occurring as felted masses within the veins, together with variable amounts of coarser haematite and, at Great Rock, minor amounts of quartz, tourmaline, pyrite, sericite and kaolinite. Cassiterite was recorded in very small amounts in the ores of the Lustleigh area, and a few grains have been separated from washed residues at Great Rock. In general, the proportion of specular haematite increases in the veins of the Lustleigh area, while pyrite is almost absent. To the north, for example at Wray Mine, the veins are entirely filled with hard specular hematite with much pyrite.

The paint ore consists of irregular plates of haematite, which, in mass appear dark steel grey or purplish grey in colour. The finer fractions of the micaceous hematite from Great Rock transmit cherry red light when mounted in Canada balsam and examined by the polarizing microscope. Much of the coarser material is opaque, though the edges of the grains may appear red. In general, the finer plates of haematite appear to have formed as overgrowths on aggregates of more granular material. Sericite (fine white mica) is quite abundant in the softer parts of the veins at Great Rock, occurring as interstitial flakes within aggregates of haematite.

There is considerable evidence from Great Rock and Kelly mines, that the earliest mineral to form in the veins was tourmaline, which was later overgrown by the more abundant haematite. The tourmaline is seen, by the polarizing microscope, as strongly zoned green or blue crystals, commonly rather broken and irregular in shape.

The presence of pyrite in the Great Rock veins is of some interest, as in some parts of the mine, it occurs as large, well-formed hemi-pyritohedra, up to 30 mm across. It has also, and even more unusually, been found as hemi-octahedra up to 10 mm across. At Wray Mine, pyrite crystals, which have been partly oxidised to red hematite, are common. Pyrite is, in all cases, formed before the haematite, but is a later mineral phase than tourmaline. Many of the veins include stringers and veinlets of quartz, which formed at a very late stage in the mineralising process.

Wallrock alteration

The granite which encloses the haematite veins shows marked alteration, with, in the rock immediately adjacent to the orebodies, disseminated haematite and chlorite together with secondary feldspar and quartz. Although the chlorite is a relatively minor mineral in the wallrock assemblage, it imparts a distinctive green hue to some areas of the granite. Examination of typical examples of wallrock using polarized light microscopy, has also shown very extensive sericitisation of the feldspars (replacement by finely crystalline white mica) in a zone extending up to a metre from the vein walls. More distal alteration commonly involves the partial alteration of feldspar to the clay mineral kaolinite, and this feature has given rise to stability problems in some parts of the Great Rock workings.

Metallogenesis

The origin of the haematite ores of north-east Dartmoor has been considered by a number of workers to represent a special case of the granite-related mineralisation of SW England. In this province, hydrothermal (that is, deposited from thermal brines) veins carry a wide variety of commodities including tin, copper, arsenic, tungsten and zinc. In the case of the northern part of Dartmoor Granite, the veins are relatively restricted in the number of minerals present (tourmaline, quartz, cassiterite, hematite, chlorite and clay minerals) and in the commodities worked (tin and micaceous hematite). A feature of the Dartmoor Granite is the sparsity of sulphide minerals in its veins; only traces of pyrite are to be found in central Dartmoor, and minor amounts at Great Rock, close to the contact of the granite with its envelope of slate. Farther out in the envelope, there are mineral veins rich in sulphides, which have yielded copper, arsenic, lead, silver and zinc. It seems that the Dartmoor Granite provided a special environment for the formation of deposits dominated by oxides and silicates. Recent work has demonstrated that hydrous fluids separating from the granite as it crystallized were extremely saline, with combined (Na + K + Ca) chloride contents of up to 50 weight %, and also, typically, with a high content of iron salts. Evidence from microthermometric studies on fluid inclusions in quartz, suggests that these fluids were progressively cooled and diluted with circulating groundwaters. Tourmaline and then cassiterite were precipitated from highly saline fluids at between 250°C and 400°C, while the specular and micaceous haematite mineralisation resulted from fluids of low salinity, with temperatures in the range 160°C to 200°C. The microthermometric studies have shown that vapour-filled inclusions are a feature of the haematite mineralisation in all localities studied: this is consistent with deposition in a steamy environment, possibly in near-fumarole conditions. The evidence suggests that the haematite mineralisation at the eastern margin of the Dartmoor Granite represents the highest and coolest level of activity of a hydrothermal system, which probably extends deep into the pluton. The type of mineralisation seen at Birch Tor in central Dartmoor represents a deeper level of hydrothermal activity that has been exposed by erosion and removal of the higher parts of the system. It is tempting to suggest that this model accounts for the presence of placer tin deposits over wide areas of western Dartmoor in which cassiterite-bearing veins have not been recorded.

CHAPTER THIRTEEN

MICACEOUS IRON OXIDE PAINTS[a]

Haematite

The mineral Haematite (Fe_2O_3), in addition to being a valuable iron ore, is used in the chemical industry. Certain massive types of the ore give a fine red ochre pigment when finely ground. The variety known as micaceous haematite, so named on account of its platy character, has some special uses. It is a black oxide of iron having a metallic lustre, a hardness of 5.5-6.6 and a specific gravity of 5.26. In different samples the plates vary in thickness with a gradual transition to specular iron ore.

Paint manufacture

When suitably crushed and ground the mineral give a black, lustrous pigment (much resembling graphite in appearance) which is used as a constituent of anti-corrosion paints, particularly for iron and steel structures.

All varieties of micaceous haematite are not equally suitable for use as protective pigments, as many have a rough texture, which makes them unsuitable for use in paints. Ideally the haematite should have a soft flaky texture and a deep black colour, even after crushing to pass a 200-mesh sieve.

Micaceous iron oxide's distinguishing feature is the unusual tabular crystal structure which can be fractured to give very thin platelet fragments, which when used as a pigment in paints orientate parallel to the paint surface. This orientation produces an increase in resistance to water permeation through paint films (and hence increased corrosion protection), reduces the ultra-violet degradation of the resin and prevents loss of film flexibility.

---

[a] This chapter is based on the following articles:

Johnstone S J, Minerals for the Chemical and Allied Industries, London, Chapman & Hall. p221, 1954.

Bishop D M, Micaceous Iron Oxide Pigments, Journal Oil & Colour Chemists Association (JOCCA) No.64, p57-64 1981

Bishop D M, Zobel, F.G.R., Micaceous Iron Oxide Paints, JOCCA March 1983, p67-86.

History

Micaceous iron oxides have always had strong connections with the railways and have been used extensively since the beginning of the 20th century as the major pigment in paints used for the protection of railway civil engineering structures all over the world. It was probably in France, about 1880, that micaceous iron oxide was first used as a pigment in paints.[1] It has been regularly used on the Eiffel Tower since its erection in 1889.[2] In 1909 twelve tons of micaceous iron oxide paints were purchased (at £30 per ton and with a covering power of 14,260 square yards per ton) for the repainting of the Hawksbury River Bridge in New South Wales, Australia.[3] It was also being used in Britain on some smaller railways, such as the Cardiff Railway and Taff Railway.[4]

In 1921 The Great Western Railway was the first major railway company to use micaceous iron oxide paints.[5] The paints were manufactured by Griffiths Bros & Co., which was formed as a paint company in 1869 and became established world-wide as suppliers of micaceous iron oxide paints under the trade name "Ferrodor" (Griffiths Bros later became part of Goodlass Wall & Co. Ltd.) Most of the early selling of "Ferrodor" to the railways was through local engineers by an agent who operated from Cardiff and was probably the reason why micaceous iron ore paints were first used on the smaller railways in the Cardiff area. One of the first bridges to be painted with micaceous iron oxide paints was Brunel's Albert Bridge at Saltash (**Page iv**) that links Devon and Cornwall across the River Tamar.[6]

The use of micaceous iron oxide paints spread on the Great Western Railway and eventually to the London, Midland and Scottish Railway where it was first used in 1929. The other railway companies probably closely followed and a London and North Eastern Railway report in 1936 stated that a micaceous iron oxide paint from Griffiths Bros. & Co.(London) Ltd (having become a limited company in 1916) had been exposed at the Forth Bridge test site.

The Devon micaceous iron oxide was used continuously up to the early 1960's when production declined and not enough was available for the paint trade. This necessitated an examination of alternative sources of micaceous iron oxide and ended the long association between the railways and the Devon pigment.

Austrian Micaceous Iron Oxide

The mine is situated at Waldenstein, on the border linking the Austrian provinces of Kaerten and Steiermark. The iron workings, which were in existence before 1150 when a castle was built for protection, were converted to the production of micaceous iron oxide pigments in 1900 and have since become renowned world-wide for the quality and quantity of the ore.

There is an interesting parallel in that, as in England, the German Railways were first introduced to micaceous iron oxide by a paint company, between 1920-1930. and there followed an extensive evaluation programme. Following highly successful exposure tests the owners of the micaceous iron oxide mines established a pigment company in 1934. the objective of the company was to produce high quality pigments that would meet the requirements of the German Railway, such as a minimum of 90 percent by weight Fe_2O_3 in the pigments, satisfactory corrosion protection, good colour stability etc..

In 1963 there was a shortage of the grade of English micaceous iron oxide pigment approved for use in British Railway's paints and samples were submitted based on the Austrian pigments so that evaluation tests could be carried out. The corrosion tests clearly showed little or no difference in the protection given by the English and Austrian pigment based paints. Approval was given in 1964 for the Waldenstein pigments to be used as an alternative.

By definition, micaceous iron oxides must possess a crystalline structure similar to mica, which itself is commonly used as an extender in paints in the form of muscovite. Mica is the name given to a group of minerals characterised by their tendency to split into platelets or lamellae. Both the English and the Austrian pigments possess this lamellar structure.

Great Rock

Great Rock produced a GRF grade (GR standing for Great Rock) which consisted of mineral that was washed through the refining process without being stamped or crushed. and the GRA grade which was the normal commercial product. Although the two grades were physically different, the thicknesses were the same (2-5 microns). The coarse GRA grade contained some platelets up to 100 microns in width, but the majority were 75 microns or less. The fine GRF grade contained a lot of fines (less than 5 microns) and a few platelets over 30 microns in width. The Austrian 'Standard' grade was remarkably similar to the Great Rock coarse or GRA grade.

Other Producers

Iron oxide pigments have been produced in Spain (Catalonia and Malaga) but these contain very little lamellar material the pigment particles being fairly uniform in size, up to 100 microns in width and thickness. South African, Japanese and West Australian pigments contain varying proportions of micaceous iron oxide and about 50 to 75 per cent is non-micaceous. Iron oxide pigments have also been produced in India and South Australia where the bulk of the pigment consists of very fine material (less than 5 microns) and cannot be considered micaceous.

The Paints

The essential requirements of early paints were:

1. They must be free from all substances that can have any injurious effect on the metal.
2. They must as far as possible be impervious to all external influences.
3. They must be sufficiently elastic to allow for expansion and contraction of metals under varying temperatures.
4. They must be hard enough not to rub off or peel off.

The basic composition of early micaceous iron oxide paints conformed to the then normal formula for an oil paint of about 65% pigment and extender and 35% boiled linseed oil and driers, and the formula remained substantially unchanged until the end of the 1920's. Extenders used over that period included slate powder, fine silica and barytes. A typical liquid drier was terebine which was originally a quick drying varnish consisting of copal with linseed oil and litharge and thinned with turpentine.

The paints were supplied either in paste form or ready-to-use. When the paste was purchased it had to be thinned in a proportion of 3 lbs paste to 1 lb thinner (special linseed oil) before application. It was recommended that:

The brush should be dipped into the paint and not only touch the surface; this would tend to keep the paint stirred in the can and so ensure an even use of the ingredients.

Although these rudimentary paints gave excellent protection over many years they suffered from two major faults, namely rapid pigment settlement and poor through drying of generously applied coatings. At that time there were no structuring agents or surfactants (surface active agents) available and the micaceous iron oxide pigment sank almost as quickly in boiled linseed oil as they did in water. The painter was advised to stir frequently the paint in the kettle, and quite arduous stirring was required before taking paint from the original container.

Analysis of Ferrodor Micaceous Iron Oxide Paint – 1928

Oil	30.5 % w/w
Volatile thinners	6.1%
Pigment	63.4%

It is appropriate to mention here that in the early part of the twentieth century, Ferrubron imported and marketed a purple MIO from Spain. This material was sold as "Natural Purple". The purple may have derived from the flakes being thin enough to transmit incident light or because the material was an iron stained mica.

The faults and inconvenience of these rudimentary MIO paints notwithstanding, the type became recognised as much superior to the early practical alternative of white lead paints for the protection of ferrous metals.

The change in the composition of the micaceous iron oxide paints from the original oil paint type to a form approximating to one in which the pigment volume was around the critical point was due to the work of Norman Bennett of Griffiths Bros & Co.. In the early twenties Bennett had observed over several years that the linseed oil film originally covering the micaceous iron oxide pigment had eroded away and that it was the exposed lamellar pigment bonded by the oil between the flakes that provided the long term protection. Experimental paints were made by pasting the micaceous iron oxide pigment in a variety of media available at that time and adjusting to a practical consistency by addition of a solvent. Exposure tests at the Ferrodor factory at Bermondsey showed that the medium had little effect on durability. These experiments gave a clear indication that, contrary to the accepted wisdom of the time, an oil medium was not essential for long term protection in micaceous iron oxide paints. The prospective use of varnish gave promise of faster drying time but not the elimination of rapid pigment settlement.

When the railways were nationalised in 1948, the paint laboratory of the former London, Midland & Scottish Railway became responsible for issuing composition specifications for the micaceous iron oxide paints to be supplied to the whole of the railway network. The objective was to replace the proprietary micaceous iron oxide paints with those purchased against specifications issued by the paint laboratory. In fact it was to be several years before only specification micaceous iron oxide paints were to be used.

London Midland Scottish Specification 1950
Undercoat

Micaceous iron oxide	42.5% w/w
Aluminium powder	6.0
Zinc oxide	1.5
Medium*	30.0
White spirit	20.0

*treated vegetable oils, resins and driers

Finishing Coat

Micaceous iron oxide	60.0% w/w
Aluminium powder	2.5
Medium	22.5
White spirit	15.0

Although the use of these specification paints spread, albeit sometimes reluctantly, through the railway network, there were still many who preferred to use proprietary micaceous iron oxide paints typified by Ferrodor.

In 1966 the system was changed and paint manufacturers were required to formulate paints to meet specified performance requirements and paint compositions were left to the manufacturers' discretion, except where indicated under specific items. A typical formulation in use in the 1980's is shown below. This was suitable for the airless spraying method of application that was replacing the traditional brush application.

Micaceous iron oxide	50.0% w/w
Extender*	6.0
Anti-settling agent	1.0
Air drying medium (solid)	18.0
Mineral spirits	24.0
Driers and anti-skinning agents	1.0

* includes barytes, talc, mica, china clay etc.

Today MIO paints are still available for specialist uses, however they no longer contain micaceous haematite from Devon.

1. Rabate, H., Travaux de Peinture, 17(5), p151, 1962.
2. Bennett, N.A., Private communication with D M Bishop.
3. Griffiths Bros Co., "Photographs of some recent Steel Structures Painted with Ferrodor Elastic Paint". Booklet October 1909.
4. Griffiths Bros Co., "Photographs of some recent Steel Structures Painted with Ferrodor Elastic Paint". Booklet October 1909.
5. Thornbery, K., private communication with D M Bishop.
6. District Civil Engineer, Exeter Division, British Rail, private communication to D M Bishop.

Chapter Fourteen

Other Micaceous Haematite Mines in Devon

A s we have seen in Chapter I and Chapter II, micaceous haematite was produced from a number of mines worked on the slopes of the Wray valley between Bovey Tracey and Moretonhampstead, and in the vicinity of Great Rock near Hennock. The sites are shown in **Figure 1**. Much of the history of the industry up to 1900 has been covered in Chapter I.

The mines of the Wray valley will only be touched on here as there are plans by the Kelly Mine Preservation Society to produce a book on Kelly Mine and the Wray Valley area. A good introduction to these mines can be found in the book – Dartmoor Mines – the Mines of the Granite Mass by Atkinson M et al, Exeter Industrial Archaeology Group, 1978.

With the exception of Kelly, these mines were insignificant as producers. All warrant further documentary and field research. If reliable printed sources of information on Great Rock can be described as limited then by comparison details on most of the operations described in this chapter are almost non-existent. The numbers in brackets after the mines' names are the grid references.

1. Mines of the Wray Valley

Hawkmoor (799818)
The mine is recorded to have started in 1892, though it is possible that mining may have taken place here much earlier. Under the name of Hawkmoor Shining Ore Mine, it was operated from 1892 to 1899 by Otto Schmidt & Co. In 1900 it was taken over by G Gartzke & Co. In 1902 it was acquired by the Ferrubron Manufacturing Co. who closed it in 1903. Throughout the whole period of working the Chief Agent was W.H.Hosking.

The mine was very small, employing a maximum of 6 men in 1892-93 and down to 3 men in 1900-01. Production from 1892 to 1901 ran at about 50 tons per year.

The mine's washing plant was located about 570 yards north of Slade Cross and on the south side of a stream flowing W.S.W. which passes under

155

the Bovey Tracey to Moretonhampstead road some 450 yds S.E. of Kelly Farm.

Kelly (796818)

Kelly was the most significant producer after Great Rock.

In 1877-81 Captain W H Hosking was the lessee and manager of Kelly Iron Mine.[1] In November 1892 J Dadd, of Kelly, Lustleigh, advertised to let the Kelly "Shining Ore" Mine. It was stated to contain several valuable lodes and was equipped with a water-wheel and stamps for dressing.[2]

The Scottish Silvoid Company commenced commercial operations at Kelly in 1900, some eight years after W.H.Hosking abandoned the mine in 1892.

Scottish Silvoid operated Kelly through to 1917, when Ferrubron took over the lease.[3] In 1901 13 workers were employed, 8 of them working underground. Presumably this was during the mining of the shaft and associated cross cuts, as employee numbers dropped to 8 the following year, and down to 2 in 1903. After that serious production seems to have started, with 10 men recorded as producing 122 tons of ore in 1904. A maximum of 202 tons was produced in 1907.[4]

After 1917 Kelly was then worked in conjunction with, and under the same management as, Great Rock. In 1938 Kelly was reported to be worked slowly and intermittently.[5] By 1944 only 2 men were working underground and mining ceased soon afterwards.

The plant at Kelly, unlike Great Rock, was not modernised. At closure the washing plant was powered by a water turbine augmented by a Blackstone oil engine. These drove an air-compressor, a winch which hauled full wagons up an incline from the bottom adit, and the stamps. Ore concentrated in settling pits was trammed across a low bridge to the drying shed where the ore was dried on a hearth as at Great Rock. A small water wheel powered a small elevator and brush sieve.

About 1950, the Moorwood lodes, then being worked as the Pepperdon Mine, were proving disappointing and the company opened a level at 'Slade' (see below) close to Kelly to provide ore supplies. This was treated in the Kelly washing plant to produce a rough concentrate which was then trucked to the modern Pepperdon plant for finishing. The operation closed in 1951/52.

This was not the end of Kelly. Fortunately the washing plant and the drying shed were not scrapped, they were just left to nature. Over the years the buildings gradually crumbled and became overgrown, visited by a few mining enthusiasts and the usual vandals who robbed the machines of their bearing brasses.

Kelly Mine Today

In 1984, the importance of the site was recognised and the Kelly Mine Preservation Society was formed with the objective of restoring the site, its buildings and equipment. Work started in 1986, and over the years thousands of man-hours have been put into the project. The washing plant and drying shed have been completely rebuilt and the machinery either replaced where missing or restored and brought back to working order. The plant today gives us a glimpse of what Great Rock would have looked like about 1935. It is a magnificent achievement, and must rank amongst the best mining conservation projects ever carried out by volunteers in this country.

Currently the underground mine is not accessible. This is, perhaps, a project for the future?

Plumley (804806)

The mine is recorded to have restarted operations in 1895 under the ownership of P J Dick, or his trustees, who worked the sett continuously until 1907 when it was taken over by Ferrubron. The mine ceased operations in August 1911. The average annual production of micaceous haematite in the years 1898-1911 was about 50 tons.

The mine worked two lodes, the northern one being the western extension of a lode in the Shaptor mine.

The Chief Agent at Plumley in 1896 was Scottish mining engineer, Alexander Livingstone. He had taken up residence in Lustleigh some years before. One presumes that he was then involved in one or more of the mines in the district, possibly Shaptor, as Plumley is only recorded as opening in 1895. Shaptor Mine was being heavily developed at that time, with 18 men employed in 1894. Perhaps he was managing the underground development there on behalf of owner Edmund Slatter?

Plumley Mine Today

Situated 650 yards W.S.W. of Shaptor Rock and on the S.E. side of the stream the mine is best approached from the Bovey Tracey to Moretonhampstead road via a rough track that leaves a small car park behind the Hawkmoor Cottages. After about 200 yards the remains of the dressing floors and settling pits can be seen below the track by the stream. Up the hillside to the S.E. are collapsed adits and an open guniss.

Shaptor (806809)

Shaptor was opened about 1892 by Nelson Bird. A year later, in 1893, E.M.Slatter is recorded as being the owner. After 1897, Slatter operated both Shaptor and Shuttamoor mines until 1902 when both were absorbed by the

Ferrubron Manufacturing Co. who operated them until closure in August 1911. Between 1894 and 1895 there was considerable investment in the two mines as indicated by a dramatic increase in the labour force from 8 in 1893 to 18 in 1894 and it was still high, at 14, in 1895. The labour levels then fell back to single figures with no more than 6 employed after 1901. With the exception of 1892 and 1893 there are no separate production figures for Shaptor as they were reported with Shuttamoor. On average Shaptor and Shuttamoor produced about 50 tons per year between them. As the combined returns for the two mines was so small there must have been long periods when only one of the mines was being worked. When production ceased in 1911 it is thought that only Shuttamoor was working.

Shaptor Mine Today
The Shaptor dressing plant is situated about 350 yards upstream from the Plumley plant site. This consists of a number of deep settling pits and foundations of several buildings extending a short way upstream. Up the hillside are a number of adits and shafts. The main adit, at GR 80618078, is identifiable by a concrete covered reservoir which formerly was the Hawkmoor Hospital water supply. The 1906 O.S. map shows a tram line running from this adit along the contour to the dressing plant.
The mine worked two lodes. The northerly lode starts at the main adit and runs slightly north of east into the hillside.
The southern lode again runs slightly north of east, and is probably an extension of the lodes worked at Plumley Mine to the west. This lode appears to have been worked from a cross cut adit running north from Grid Reference 80878065.[6]

Wray (771848) and Moorwood (776837)
The mines at Wray and Moorwood appear only to have been worked in the 20th Century. Information regarding their history is confused and, at times, contradictory. To make matters worse, Moorwood was worked under the name of Pepperdon even though Pepperdon Farm is very close to the Wray Mine.
A 'Wraybarton' mine was worked from 1920 until 1925 by the Wray Ferric Oxide Mine Ltd.. In June 1922 it was reported that

> *Wray Ferric Oxide Mines Ltd. had been formed to acquire and take over, as a going concern, the business now carried out at Wray Barton Farm, Moretonhampstead, Devon under the style or name of the Wray Ferric Oxide Mine.*[7]

Under the name 'Wray', a mine began operations in 1928 producing red ochre and continued through the 1930's employing 4 or 5 persons. The Wray Mining Co. Ltd. was registered on 11th June 1928 and extended into Lustleigh.[8] 'Wraybarton' and 'Wray' mines were probably the same site.[9] Dines[10] says:

> *Wray Mine on the eastern slopes of the Wray Brook was opened up in 1929 by an adit, with portal 250 yards N.E. of Wray Barton and developed for a short distance a micaceous haematite lode.......but the amount of ore raised was found to be too hard and granular for paint making and further lodes were sought.*

In 1931 the company began exploration for additional deposits and located promising lodes of micaceous haematite in Moor wood.

An undated report at the British Geological Survey, Exeter states:

> *Several lodes, consisting of interlaced veins from 2 to 15 ins. wide, course about E.6 degrees N. and dipping steeply north but only one at present being worked. This is up to 8 ins wide and has been opened up by means of 2 levels driven eastwards into the hillside; the shallow level had been driven about 60 fms and the deep level, 13 fms below about 30 fms by 1938. A winze sunk from the upper level and a rise up from the lower pass each other 18 ft apart due to following different strings of ore.*

There is now a gap until 1941 when Roy Nicol appeared on the scene and took out a lease to mine throughout the area of Pepperdon Farm to East Wray Barton, for iron ore and shining ore.[11] Roy Nicol was, at this time associated with a Mr New in a company Nicol and New Ltd., 81 Gracechurch Street, London, EC3.[12]

Mining then started at Moorwood (Pepperdon Mine) and Elias Tucker (jnr), brother of 'Old Charlie' Tucker of Great Rock took a prominent part in opening the mine.[13]

We know that mining was taking place at Moorwood in 1942 as Pocock wrote in January 1942:

> *Moorwood Mines – Pepperdon estate, Moretonhampstead. At this locality, near Wray Barton, good quality micaceous iron-ore is being mined ....by Messrs. Nicol and New Ltd.[14]*

The working did not last long for in the List of Mines (1945) Pepperdon is reported as ' Discontinued 1944'. In the late 1940's the mine was re-opened by the same company. At some point in the 1940's a new plant was built at Moorwood. It is not clear when this was, however it would have been difficult to have sourced the equipment for the mill during the war. Results of the new workings underground were disappointing and the company were soon casting around for sources of ore to supply the mill. Some ore was produced from a new development at 'Slade', a few hundred yards S.W. of Kelly Mine.

Lack of ore caused the operation to cease early in 1952. The machinery was stripped from the mill, and for some years the building was used as a barn by a local farmer. In early 1974 the mill building was being dismantled and by the middle of that year it was evident that a dwelling house was being built on the site.[15]

Wray Mine Today

Going from Moretonhampstead to Bovey Tracey on the A382, after passing under the line of the railway take the first turning on the left - signed 'unsuitable for motors'. After an ascent of about half a mile, a footpath is signposted on the right of the road. Going down the footpath for about 30 yds, the mine dressing floors can be found over the bank on the left in the corner of Wray wood. This has public access and is the property of Devon County Council.[16]

Plate 63 – Wray Mine dressing floors looking south west 1999. In the foreground are three buddles, the stack in the background was for a small drying shed. (© Author)

The dressing floors include the foundations of several mine buildings and 3 round buddles. **Plate 63.** Immediately above the dressing floors is the entrance (now run-in) to a short blind drive, it is recorded[17] that there were small workings off it. Above the mill is a masonry lined tank, that presumably held water for the plant. From the dressing floors the line of a tramway can be followed along the contour (not the more modern bulldozed road) to the portal of the main adit some 200 yds. to the east. There is a second adit on the same lode some 50 ft up the hillside. The lower level is open but gated. The upper level is collapsed and there is a further collapse to surface up slope from the site of the portal. From the entrance of the upper level the line of a second tramway can be traced back along the hillside towards the mill until it is cut by a modern bulldozed track. A few lengths of rail were lying beside part of this new track in May 2002.

Moorwood (Pepperdon) Mine Today
The mine is located in private woodland, about 500 yards S.W. of Lewdons Farm, and some way to the south of Wray.
The Pepperdon mill, now a private house, still retains the two separate floor levels of the original mill. Behind the house is a block containing the mine office, miners dry, store rooms and a generator room. The site has the appearance of major investment in buildings and equipment.[18]

The underground workings at Moorwood[19]
There are five adits currently (2002) accessible on the property.
The workings on the Main Lode provide domestic water supply to a number of properties so it is essential that permission is obtained to visit the site. The northernmost adit is adjoining the old mine buildings. It was driven in for about 200 feet. No orebodies worth stoping were encountered.
In the wood above the access track to the mill site are to be found the magazine and detonator store constructed from white Candy brick, with the remains of the wooden doors and shelving. To the south of these are three adits on the Main Lode. The lowest was probably the main tramming level and there are faint traces of an incline down to the main access track. This was reported to have been worked by a hand winch.[20/a] Above this the next adit is the most extensive, outside on the tip are the fragments of a side-tipping wagon. The highest adit is a short low drive under a boulder and connects, probably just for ventilation, into the stopes below. **Figure 25** is a survey of the Main Lode workings carried out by the Plymouth Caving Group in 2002. Only a small amount of ground has been stoped out. One

[a] This winch is now in a private collection in Torquay

wonders why the bottom level was not driven further as this appears to offer the best opportunity to locate mineable ore.

Just above and to the south of the middle adit on Main Lode is an exploratory adit on a southern lode. This is only about 120 feet long and there is no stoping.

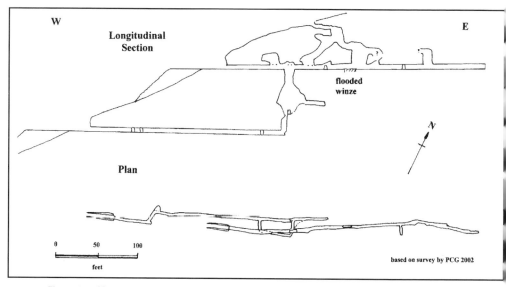

Figure 25 – Moorwood Mine. The three adits of Main Lode Workings – 2002.

Slade 797816

The name 'Slade' has been adopted by the Kelly Mine Preservation Society to differentiate it from Kelly and Hawkmoor.

The mine was opened by Messrs. Nicols and New who were then engaged in working Pepperdon Mine. Underground working was confined to an adit driven on the westward extension of the Hawkmoor Mine lodes some 600 yard south of Kelly Mine, just above the main road to Bovey Tracey.

Ore from the adit was taken by lorry to Kelly for cleaning and crushing before being taken to the modern plant at Pepperdon for the final dressing, drying and bagging.

In 1951, blasting in the level broke into 'old men's workings'. Unfortunately, the breaking into the old workings coincided with the collapse of the top of the stope that they were working. This brought work to a halt and led also to the closure of Pepperdon Mine.[21]

Slade Today

Just to the north of the main road is a collapsed adit with a tramway, complete with track and point-work, along the hillside round to a waste dump above the stream. There is also the remains of the ore-chute down to the lorry-loading bay by the road. Up the hill above the adit is a large collapse to surface up on the line of the workings.

Other workings in the Wray Valley

In addition to the mines mentioned above there is evidence of workings at Higher Knowle, Casley Court, Elsford, Higher Coombe, Laployd Down and Stoneland Waste.

2. Mines around Great Rock

Bowden Hill (917808 – 822810)

The 19th Century history of this mine has been covered in Chapter I.

A Higher Bowden Mine was worked by C.Funget in 1927-8 but no figures of output are available.[22]

This ties in with the Mining Journal report for 1927:[23]

> *Bowder* (sic) *mine and Great Rock mine are both producing vigorously, and there are several other small properties producing haematite in the parishes of Lustleigh and Hennock.*

It is presumed that 'Bowder' is a corruption of Bowden. Sam Bradford recalled[24]

> *There was a mine up there up on that top road that goes down to Shaptor Farm. A Frenchman came over not long ago*[b]*...and opened up that old mine. He thought that he was going to get a lot more out of it, and he employed 2 or 3 blokes there working and he built a place right down Hyner there where you go into the old mine....that lane....he had stamps....Frenchman he was called Funget.*[c] *There was a big shed where they go into Great Rock down there....opposite was a big shed....he put in stamps and all in there, and a washing plant and all. When they opened up that old mine, they did not find what they thought that they were going to get – it had all been worked out.*

---

[b] This is an example of how oral history on its own can be misleading if taken literally. 'Not long ago' was referring to an event 65 years previously!
[c] A french company, Funget, is listed today (2002) as a supplier of anti-corrosion paints.

Bowden Hill Today

The surface workings can be traced by a line of old pits (many now partly filled) 600 yds long commencing near the road, 350 yds. S.E. of Beadon Cross and running approximately E.N.E. with its centre 1,100 yards west of Hennock Churchyard. There is the remains of what appears to be the adit, with micaceous haematite in the dump, 200 yds N.W. of Chericombe Cross. The location of Engine Shaft (see **Figure 4**) and the adjacent adit shaft cannot be identified. There is the suggestion of further workings further W.S.W on the projected strike of the lode close to the access road to Shaptor Farm, and to the east across Beadon Lane.

Shuttamoor (823829)

There is almost nothing in print about the history of this mine.

The centre of the mine is situated about 400 yds E.S.E. of Shuttamoor farm. Whilst recorded working started in 1897, the presence of an old shaft marked on the 1890 First edition Ordnance Survey map indicates that it must have been worked much earlier. In 1897, Shuttamoor was re-opened by E M Slatter, then operating Shaptor mine, and Slatter worked the mine until the takeover by Ferrubron in 1902.

A plan and a longitudinal section have survived (**Figure 26 & 27**). These are undated but are thought to date from about 1900. The reservoir, smith's

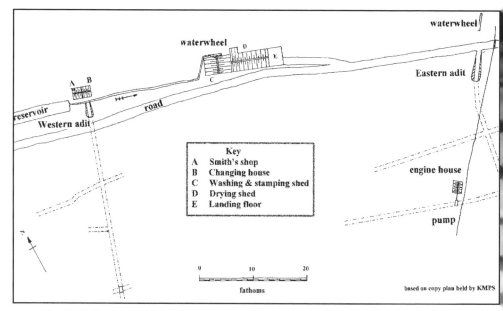

Figure 26 – Shuttamoor Mine – Plan of Workings about 1900.

shop and the washing/drying shed shown on the plan all appear on the Second Edition Ordnance Survey map but are absent from the 1890 map. The pump shaft at the eastern end of the mine is the same shaft as the one shown as 'Old Shaft' in 1890. The engine house, shown adjacent to the pump shaft, presumably housed a small steam engine operating a short flat rod to the top of the shaft. The section shows a bucket lift pumping to adit with two short levels below adit. The plan also shows a waterwheel down by the stream. It is directly in line with the shaft and it is suggested that this might have been an earlier power source for the pump.

Whilst the title of the plan is 'Plan of Workings', it only shows adit level and is very much a sketch rather than a surveyed plan. The longitudinal section on 'South Lode' shows some concentrated stoping around the area of the pump shaft. This again is sketched not surveyed.

Plate 5 (Chapter Three) is a rare photograph taken in the Shuttamoor dressing plant about 1910 and is contemporary with the photo taken at Great Rock about 1902 (**Plate 6**) The layout shown in the photograph was probably typical of these little mines. The ore from the mine was washed through a screen into a trough or strip and the mineral bearing oversize from the screen then being crushed in a small waterwheel driven set of Californian stamps. The stamps here are similar to those shown at Great Rock and the set which have been preserved at Kelly. The roof over the stamps has the same orientation as shown on the mine plan.

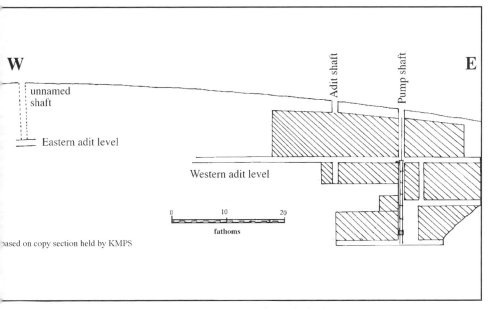

Figure 27 – Shuttamoor Mine – longitudinal Section of 'South' Lode about 1900

Sam Bradford recalled that William Hosking lived out at Shuttamoor when the mine was working. *Had to sink – a lot of water.* The lodes lie just to the south of the stream below Shuttamoor farm. Adit level is quite shallow and the easily worked lode above adit would have been mined out at an early stage. Sustained production would have meant sinking below adit with the concomitant problem of pumping. Shuttamoor and Kelly are the only MIO mines known to have put in pumping plant.

The mine finally closed in 1911 just after, but not necessarily because of, the accident that killed Elias Tucker.

Great Rock did some prospecting here in 1967-9 in a last desperate attempt to find additional ore.

Shuttamoor Mine Today

Take Bell Lane out of Hennock, turn right at Chericombe Head down Beadon Lane past the Great Rock Beadon workings. Turn right just before the reservoir and the road leads to Shuttamoor Farm. Just before the stream a gate on the right hand side of the road accesses a faint track across a field that leads to the site.

The mine is in the wood at the end of the field. Immediately obvious on entering the wood are a number of fenced areas above the track which mark where stoping has broken through to surface. The site takes some interpreting as the slope above the track is now conifer forest and the area between the track and the stream is very overgrown. Referring to **Figure 26** the first clearly identifiable point is the cutting into the blocked Western adit and a large waste dump from the adit running east into the stream. The smith's shop and changing house have vanished. To the east of the adit the now dry reservoir can clearly be seen. Some 70 yards further down the track a levelled area below the track marks the site of the washing and drying plant. Only fragments of a couple of retaining walls remain.

A further 80 yards or so further down the track the infilled Eastern adit can be seen on the right hand side of the track just before an obvious old boundary wall. A trench below the track marks the possible site of the waterwheel. Up above the track the pump shaft is still open although there is no sign of the building that housed the pump.

It is clear that far more mining has taken place than is indicted on **Figure 27**. There are two lines of collapses and open gunnises extending much further east of the Eastern and Western adit workings. Stoping has been carried almost to surface right along the strike of the lodes.

Continuing along the track into the clearing, the track divides with the left fork crossing the river. An adit lies on the corner of this junction. To the left of the track, across the bridge is a small settling tank.

Sycamore (Vicinity of 825828?)
A small mine of which nothing appears to be known beyond the fact that it was somewhere near Shuttamoor.[25]

1. Hunts's Mineral Statistics 1877-81.
2. Mining Journal, 26th November 1892.
3. Atkinson M et al, Dartmoor Mines – the Mines of the Granite Mass, Exeter Industrial Archaeology Group, 1978 p38.
4. KMPS Newsletter, September 2001.
5. British Geological Survey files – Exeter.
6. Walter N. The remains of Shaptor Mine, Kelly Mine Preservation Society Newsletter, March 2000,
7. Mining Journal, 24th June 1922, p479.
8. Mining World, 23rd June 1928.
9. Atkinson M et al, Dartmoor Mines – the Mines of the Granite Mass, Exeter Industrial Archaeology Group, 1978 p46.
10. Dines H.G., The Metalliferous Mining Region of South-West England. HMSO 1056. p725.
11. Information was obtained from the deeds of Willowrey Farm: Kelly Mine Preservation Society Newsletter, September 1996.
12. Kelly Mine Preservation Society Newsletter, September 1996.
13. Letter from Ron Tucker to Bob le Marchant, 25 January 2000. Kelly Mine Preservation Society Newsletter, June 2000.
14. Pocock R., Ochres, Umbers, and other Natural Earth Pigments of England and Wales, Geological Survey Of Great Britain – Wartime Pamphlet No.21. January 1942.
15. Richardson P.H.G., Mines of Dartmoor and the Tamar Valley. British Mining Vol.44, NMRG, 1991 p68.
16. Atkinson M et al, Dartmoor Mines – the Mines of the Granite Mass, Exeter Industrial Archaeology Group, 1978 p46.
17. Atkinson M et al, Dartmoor Mines – the Mines of the Granite Mass, Exeter Industrial Archaeology Group, 1978 p46.
18. Walter N., Report on KMPS Visit, 19th March, 2000. Kelly Mine Preservation Society Newsletter, May 2000.
19. Draft report by Alasdair Neill, PCG, copied to the author, October 2002.
20. Atkinson M. et al, Dartmoor Mines – The Mines of the Granite Mass, Exeter Industrial Archaeology group, 1978 p41.
21. Westaway d., The Recollections of Mr. Francis Heath. Kelly Mine Preservation Society Newsletter, November 1995.
22. Atkinson K et al., Dartmoor Mines,1977. p47.
23. Mining Journal, 7 January, 1928.
24. Interview – Sam Bradford, 26 July 1993, B Brett.
25. Richardson P.H.G. Mines of Dartmoor and the Tamar Valley. British Mining Vol.44, NMRG, 1991 p69.

William Henry Hosking was born in 1839 at Lydford, West Devon. In 1881 he was living in Wolborough Street, Newton Abbot with his wife, Emily, aged 42 and their children, Emily Florence (18), William Henry (13), Lillie (4) and John (2). By 1897 he had moved to a house, Pevensey, overlooking Courtenay Park in Newton Abbot. He died in 1925.

Mining Interests of W H Hosking in the West Country
Mines are in Devon unless stated otherwise

Mine	Position		Listed Owner
Sigford Consols (Cu)	Chief Agent	1860-62	
Smiths Wood (Sn)	Chief Agent	1860-62	
Ashburton United (Sn, As)	Manager	1864-66	
Devon Wheal Frances (Cu)	Chief Agent	1869-72	
Killivreth (Fe) (Cornwall)	Chief Agent	1870-71	The Ironmasters Co.
Alma (Fe) (Cornwall)	Chief Agent	1870-71	Faithful, Cookson & Co.
West Brixham (Fe)	Chief Agent	1870-72	Van Iron Ore Co.
South Devon (Fe)	Chief Agent	1870-76	"
Hennock (Fe)	Chief Agent	1870-73	"
Salcombe (Fe)	Chief Agent	1870-72	"
Ladock (Fe) (Cornwall)	Chief Agent	1870-71	Faithful, Cookson & Co.
	Manager	1872-76	
Pawton (Fe) (Cornwall)	Chief Agent	1873-74	Native Iron Ore Co.
Brixham (Fe)	Chief Agent	1871-73	Welsh Iron Works
		1873	Cookson & Co.
Colvreath (Fe) (Cornwall)	Manager	1872-75	The Ironmasters Co.
Treverbyn (Fe) (Cornwall)	Manager	1873-76	Worked with Ladock
Smallacombe (Fe)	Manager	1873-77	Native Iron Ore Co.
Wolborough (Fe)	Chief Agent	1874-76	Lowther Iron Ore Co.
West Coombe Martin (Pb) (Somerset)	Chief Agent	1877	
Great Wheal Eleanor (Sn)	Chief Agent	1877-83	
Kelly (MH)	Chief Agent	1877-92	Kelly Iron Co.
	Owner 1879	1882-92	
Park Valley (Pb/Ag)	Manager	1878-81	Park Valley mining Co.
Stancombe (Mn)	Chief Agent	1879-81	Richards & Power
Owlacombe (Cu Sn)	Chief Agent	1882-83	Sir H Hoare
Hawkmoor (MH)	Chief Agent	1892-1902	Schmidt & Co 1892-99
			Gartzke & Co. 1900-01
			Ferrubron 1902-03
Great Rock (MH)	Chief Agent	1896-19??	As Hawkmoor
			Ferrubron after 1902.

Ford Farm (As)	Chief Agent	1898-1903	Sir H Hoare
Shaptor and Shuttamoor (MH)	Secretary	1903-11	Ferrubron
	Chief Agent	1909-11	
Plumley (MH)	Secretary	1907-11	Ferrubron
	Chief Agent	1909-11	
Albion* (Sn)	Manager	1913	Albion Tin Syndicate

*W H Hosking's son, also called William Henry Hosking established his own business as a mining agent in Ashburton in 1910. It is possible that Albion was managed by W H Hosking (junior)

Appendix II

Some Notes on Micaceous Iron Ore, by Sherard Cowper-Coles

Micaceous iron ore, to which has also been given a number of fancy names, such as shining ore, ferolite, etc., contains about 95 per cent. of rustless peroxide of iron. and is found in considerable quantities in Devonshire. The following is an analysis of a sample obtained from that county:

	%
Moisture	0.128
Combined water	0.486
Silica	0.959
Fe_2O_3	96.723
Alumina	0.766
CaO	0.283
MgO	0.043
SO_3	0.332 – 0.133 p.c. sulphur
P_2O_5	0.086 – 0.037 phosphorus
MnO	0.017
CuO	0.018
NiO	0.009
	99.890

The veins in Devonshire, as a rule, are of no great width. and constantly pinch out; the ore is quite soft and readily crushed, and after washing is packed into barrels and sent to the works, where it is made into paint, as it is now being extensively used for coating iron and steel structures. The best qualities of the ore realise about £12 per ton.

The micaceous iron is non-magnetic, and after being kept at a bright red heat for a considerable time is not changed; nitric and sulphuric acid has (sic) little or no effect upon it, either cold or boiling, but the ore is dissolved very gradually in strong hydrochloric acid.

Mining Journal 8 January 1898

APPENDIX **III**

People who worked at Great Rock

Adcock Fred	Miner until May 1954 when had an accident due to a fall of ground. then surface worker.
Adcock Gerald	Miner – 2 weeks notice 30/6/69
Allen T G	1909 at Shuttamoor then Gt Rock
Aplin Rene	Worked in the mill – 1948-1949
Atkinson Stephen	Vacation student April 1963
Avery T	Working on launders Sept 1934
Ball Arthur	Mine engineer 1949-1969. Came from Bridford Mine, one month notice 30/6/69
Ball Harold	Miner
Beard Sid	Miner
Bellamy Alan	Surface worker
Bellamy Dave	Miner
Bellamy Tom	Pre-war
Bellamy Charlie	Miner 1933
Bellamy Rene	Worked in the washing plant during WWII
Bellamy Ron	Miner
Bishop	Journeyman blacksmith
Bovey Joe	Surface worker
Bowden Terry	Miner about 1962
Bradford Sam	27/2/52 aged 53 accident on surface as result of a fire in the workman's hut.
Bradford Sally	Worked for 28 years. First in washing plant and then as the Canteen lady
Brock Henry	£10 in 1933 will
Brooks Tony	Vacation student April 1963.
Browning A	One week notice 30/6/69
Bunclarke Tony	Miner 1955-1958 & 1960-1969. One week notice 30/6/69
Burgoyne Ian	Miner
Burgoyne Mike	Miner
Carroll T	One week notice 30/6/69
Caunter Mike	Miner
Chappel John	1910
Chubb Bill	Miner from Cornwall
Chubb Arnold	Miner from Cornwall
Cole Stanley	£5 in 1933 will..died of silicosis
Coles Bill	Killed 1945/46 in a roof fall at Beadon
Counter Fred	1910
Cudmore Albert Henry	Left £10 in 1933 will. Aged 55, died of silicosis inquest 12/12/35
Cudmore Archie	
Davey J A	1951 aged 33 underground accident

Daw Ern	1910
Dean Alfred	Surface worker
Dexter ?	Briefly underground then general surface duties and lorry driver 1930's
Down Ern	Lorry driver 1930's
Gammon A	2 weeks notice 30/5/69
Gardener Ernest	£2 10s. in 1933 will.
Gayle Freddie	Miner 1960's
Gillham Milburn Thomas Elias	£10 in 1933 will. Aged 30, died of silicosis inquest 12/12/35
Gloyn Fred	1910
Gloyn Jack	1910
Godfrey Stan	Miner 1962-69, Union rep 1969
Godolphin Betty	Washing shed – wartime
Hancock	
Haydon-Baillie Tony	Summer 1962
Haydon-Baillie Wensley	Summer 62- Spring 63
Haywood Harold	Miner
Hellier A	1910
Hellier Claude	Miner 1960's
Hewitt Sally	Canteen lady
Hine P	
Hine W	Miner then Foreman. 1917-1960. Moved over from Kelly.
Hodge Alfred Edward	1933 – 1939. £5 in 1933 will.
Hodge Frederick Charles	£10 in 1933 will, working on launders Sept 1934
Hollins Bernard	
Hooper Reginald George Henry	£10 in 1933 will
Horrell Douglas	Miner
Isaacs ?	Trammer pre-war
James William Henry	£2 10s. in 1933 will.
Joy Cecil	
Joyce A	One week notice 30/6/69
Lawrence Donald	Miner
Lawrence Reg	Surface worker
Miller Bill	Stoping pre-war
Moyle Rex	
Muir Flora	Mill worker 1945
Payne Jack	Miner 1960's
Palmer F	Splicing rope and cleaning Office, 1934
Penfold Harry	Surface worker
Philpott P	One Week notice 30/6/69
Pike M	1933
Pike William James	£10 in 1933 will
Potter Cecil	Miner
Potter Dave	Miner. One weeks notice 30/6/69
Potter Norman	Surface worker
Potter Sidney	Surface worker
Preston Cyril	Died of silicosis

Preston Edwin	Boy about 1948
Preston Fred	Surface worker
Preston Gilbert Reginald	£10 in 1933 will.
Preston Sidney	Surface worker 1916-1969. Left £10 in will 1933. Surface worker accident about 1955
Purdon G	Contract miner 1933
Raisey Henry	Miner 1962
Rice Charlie	Miner
Rice Thomas Henry	£10 in 1933 will
Sampson Ern	1910
Sampson Lewis George	£10 in will 1933.
Sampson Lloyd	£10 in 1933 will.
Sampson William Reginald	£10 in 1933 will.
Sanders C	1933
Sandicott	
Sexton Edward John	£5 in 1933 will.
Slatter Edmund Meek	Died 19.12.33
Slocombe Oliver (snr)	Surface worker
Slocombe Oliver (jnr)	Surface worker
Stancombe George	In charge of GR drying sheds – lived in one of the bungalows
Stancombe (snr) Jim	1910
Stancombe (jnr) Jim	1910
Taylor Sid	Manager 1949-1966
Tucker Elias	Mine Foreman, killed at Shuttamoor 11th February 1911
Tucker Charlie George	"Old Man" Tucker,. Mine Foreman 1911-1934, Mine manager 1934-1942. £50 in will 1933.
Tucker Charles Frederick	"Young Charlie" £20 in will 1933, Mine manager 1942-1948
Tucker Ron	Son of "Young" Charlie Tucker.
Underhill Frank	Surface worker
Walling J	1933
Warren Phyllis	Mill worker 1945
Weatherdon William	Left £10 in 1933 will
Webber Walter Lionel	£10 in will 1933. Aged 38 died of silicosis inquest 12/12/35
Wills David	Surface worker 1955-1957.
Wills Dave	Miner
Wills Ern	1910
Wills William Henry	£10 in 1933 will. Mine Foreman. Mine Manager 1966-69
Wills William Francis Charles	Surface worker. £5 in 1933 will.
Winslade Arthur	Lorry driver 1933
Wonnacott Percy	Miner. Tramming accident
Yeoman Peter	1956-1969 as underground miner, accident 1969

FURTHER READING

Atkinson M. et al	Dartmoor Mines – The Mines of the Granite Mass, 1978.
Beer K.E & Scrivener R.C.	Metalliferous Mineralisation 117-147, in E. M Durrance and D.J.C. Laming (editors), The Geology of Devon, University of Exeter: Exeter 1982
Bishop D.M.,	Micaceous Iron Oxide Pigments, JOCCA No.64, 1981, p57-64.
Bishop D.M. & Zobel F.G.R.	Micaceous Iron Oxide Paints, JOCCA March 1983, p67-86.
Burt et al,	Devon and Somerset Mines, University of Exeter Press, 1984.
Cantrill T.C. et al	Iron Ores of Devon & Cornwall, Mineral Resources Vol XIV, London HMSO 1919.
Chesley J.T. et al	Thermochronology of the Cornubian batholith in southwest England: implications for pluton emplacement and protracted hydrothermal mineralization. Geochimica et Cosmochimica Acta, 57, 1817-1835. 1993.
Clark S.,	Mining and Quarrying in the Teign Valley, Orchard Publications, 1995,
Collins J.H.	Observations on the West of England Mining Region, Trans. RGSC, 1912.
De La Beche H.T.	Report on the Geology of Cornwall, Devon and West Somerset. Mem. Geol. Surv. 1839.
Dines H.G.	Metalliferous Mining Region of SW England, HMSO, 1956.
Edwards R.A. & Scrivener R.C.	The Geology of the Country around Exeter, Memoir of the British Geological Survey, Sheet 325 (England and Wales), 1999.
Hamilton Jenkin A.K.	Mines of Devon – North and East Dartmoor, Devon Library Services, Exeter, 1981.
Henson F.A.	On the Occurrance of Micaceous Haematite in the Hennock-Lustleigh Area, Eastern Dartmoor, Proc. Geol. Assoc. Vol 67, 1956.
Johnstone S.J. & Johnstone M.G.	Minerals for the Chemical and Allied Industries, London, Chapman & Hall. 1961.
MacAlister D.A.	Note on the Association of Cassiterite and Specular Iron in the lodes of Dartmoor, Geological Magazine, 5, 6, 402-409. 1909.
Martin J.S.	Micaceous Iron Ore Near Bovey Tracey, Trans. Manchester Geological Soc. Vol.23 (1895).
Richardson P.H.G.	Mines of Dartmoor and the Tamar Valley, British Mining Vol.44, NMRG, 1991.
Schmitz C.	The Teign Valley Silver-Lead Mines, 1806-1880, British Mining No.15, NMRS, 1980.
Scrivener R.C.	Tin and Related Mineralisation of the Dartmoor Granite, Unpublished Ph.D. Thesis: University of Exeter. 1982
Selwood et al	The Geology of the Country around Newton Abbot, Mem. Geol. Surv., HMSO 1984.
Ussher W.A.E.	The Geology of the Country Around Newton Abbot, Mem. Geol. Surv. 1913.

INDEX